Exercises in

SET THEORY

by

L. E. SIGLER
Hofstra University

D. VAN NOSTRAND COMPANY, INC.
PRINCETON, NEW JERSEY
TORONTO NEW YORK LONDON

D. VAN NOSTRAND COMPANY, INC.
120 Alexander St., Princeton, New Jersey (*Principal office*)
24 West 40 Street, New York 18, New York

D. VAN NOSTRAND COMPANY, LTD.
358, Kensington High Street, London, W.14, England

D. VAN NOSTRAND COMPANY (CANADA), LTD.
25 Hollinger Road, Toronto 16, Canada

Published simultaneously in Canada by
D. VAN NOSTRAND COMPANY (Canada), LTD.

PRINTED IN THE UNITED STATES OF AMERICA

PREFACE

These exercises are intended to assist students in understanding the elements of set theory. The arrangement of topics follows the development found in Paul Halmos' *Naive Set Theory*, al-hough a student studying some other textbook should find the problems useful. The exercises are, on the whole, routine explorations of the definitions and theorems of set theory and are not puzzle or contest problems. The problems vary somewhat in difficulty, but nearly all should yield to the average student, provided he is endowed also with persistence. It is the author's belief that maximal benefit will accrue to the student who does not look at the answers before he himself has some solution to check. A sense of pride in this matter on the student's part will be a productive attitude for him. There are, of course, multiple answers possible for many problems, while only one is offered in the answer section. Perhaps the student may happily find more elegant solutions than those given.

At the beginning of each chapter there is a brief compilation of results taken from *Naive Set Theory* (NST) and sometimes elsewhere that are relevant to the exercises of that chapter. There are exercises in algebra involving monoids, semigroups, groups, rings, ields, vector spaces, and algebras. All necessary definitions are included, but references to helpful books are also included. These algebraic exercises are included in expectation that the student will have previously completed an undergraduate course or two in algebra and will profit from applications of the abstract concepts of set theo-y to the familiar. In the chapter on ordinals the exercises lead to a proof of the compatibility of the recursive and set theoretic treatments of ordinal arithmetic. Although it ought to be obvious, it will be stated hat no originality is claimed for the exercises.

L. E. S.

Table Showing Relationship of
Exercises to Set Theory Text

Exercises in Set Theory	*Naive Set Theory*
Chapter	Section
1	1-5
2	6
3	7
4	8
5	9
6-7	10
8	11-13
9	14
10	15-16
11	17
12	18
13	19-21
14	22-25

CONTENTS

Preface

1. Elementary Concepts 1
2. The Ordered Pair and the Cartesian Product 9
3. Relations 11
4. Functions 16
5. Families 22
6. Functions Defined on Power Sets 24
7. Applications of Functions 26
8. The Natural Numbers 33
9. Order 39
10. The Axiom of Choice and Zorn's Lemma 42
11. Well Ordering 44
12. Transfinite Recursion and Similarity 47
13. Ordinals 51
14. Cardinals 59

Answers 63

References 133

Index 135

CHAPTER I

ELEMENTARY CONCEPTS

1.0 $x \in A$ reads x is a member (or element) of set A. (NST p2)

$x \notin A$ reads x is not a member of set A. (NST p2)

Axiom of Extension. $A = B$ means $x \in A$ iff (if and only if) $x \in B$. (NST p2)

Definition of Subsets. $A \subset B$ means if $x \in A$ then $x \in B$. (NST p3)

$A \subsetneq B$ means $A \subset B$ and $A \neq B$, A is a proper subset of B.

If $S(y)$ is a condition, then $x \in \{y|\ S(y)\}$ iff $S(x)$. (NST pp4, 10)

Axiom of Specification. If A is a set and $S(x)$ is a condition, then $\{x|\ x \in A$ and $S(x)\}$ is a set. (NST p60)

Axiom of Pairing. If A and B are sets, then there exists a set C so that $A \in C$ and $B \in C$. (NST p9)

Definition of Pair. $\{A, B\} = \{x|\ x = A$ or $x = B\}$. (NST p9)

Axiom of Unions. If $\mathcal{C}$ is a set, then there exists a set U such that if $x \in X$ for some $X \in \mathcal{C}$, then $x \in U$. (NST p12)

Definition of Union. $\bigcup \mathcal{C} = \{x|\ x \in X$ for some $X \in \mathcal{C}\}$. (NST p12)

Definition of Intersection. For $\mathcal{C} \neq \phi$, $\bigcap \mathcal{C} = \{x|\ x \in X$ for all $X \in \mathcal{C}\}$. (NST p15)

Definition of Relative Complement. $A - B = \{x|\ x \in A$ and $x \notin B\}$. (NST p17) If the set A is understood from context, denote $A - B$ by B'.

Axiom of Powers. If E is a set, then there exists a set P such that if $X \subset E$, then $X \in P$. (NST p19)

Definition of Power Set. $\mathcal{P} E = \{x \mid x \subset E\}$. (NST p19)

Definition of the Empty Set. $\emptyset = \{x \mid x \neq x\}$.

1.1 The following symbols are often used to study the algebra of sentences:

$\wedge$	representing	and
$\vee$	representing	or
$\neg$	representing	not
$\Longrightarrow$	representing	if ... then ..., implies
$\Longleftrightarrow$	representing	if and only if
$\exists$	representing	there exists, for some
$\forall$	representing	for all

These symbols are employed according to the following rules of construction for sentences. If p and q are sentences, then $p \wedge q$, $p \vee q$, $\neg p$, $p \Longrightarrow q$, $p \Longleftrightarrow q$ are sentences. If p is a sentence, then $\exists x: p$, $\forall x: p$ are sentences. For example, given that p, q, r are sentences, it is verified that $\neg [(p \wedge \neg q) \vee r]$ is a sentence in the following way. q is a sentence; therefore $\neg q$ is a sentence. p and $\neg q$ are sentences; therefore $p \wedge \neg q$ is a sentence. $p \wedge \neg q$ and r are sentences; therefore $(p \wedge \neg q) \vee r$ is a sentence. $(p \wedge \neg q) \vee r$ is a sentence; therefore $\neg [(p \wedge \neg q) \vee r]$ is a sentence.

The truth values of the sentences constructed from the first five symbols are determined formally from defining truth tables. These are (using 1 as a symbol for true and 0 for false):

p	q	$p \wedge q$
1	1	1
1	0	0
0	1	0
0	0	0

p	q	$p \vee q$
1	1	1
1	0	1
0	1	1
0	0	0

p	$\neg p$
1	0
0	1

p	q	$p \Longrightarrow q$
1	1	1
1	0	0
0	1	1
0	0	1

p	q	$p \Longleftrightarrow q$
1	1	1
1	0	0
0	1	0
0	0	1 .

For example, if p is a false sentence and q is a true sentence, then $p \wedge q$, $p \Longleftrightarrow q$ are false and $p \Longrightarrow q$, $p \vee q$, $\neg p$ are true.

Two sentences with the same truth values are equivalent ($\equiv$). Equivalences can be systematically verified using the truth tables iteratively as in these examples.

$$p \Longrightarrow q \equiv \neg p \vee q$$

p	q	$p \Longrightarrow q$	$\neg p$	$\neg p \vee q$
1	1	1	0	1
1	0	0	0	0
0	1	1	1	1
0	0	1	1	1

The column for $p \Longrightarrow q$ and the column for $\neg p \vee q$ contain the same truth values.

$$p \Longrightarrow q \equiv \neg q \Longrightarrow \neg p$$

p	q	$\neg q$	$\neg p$	$\neg q \Longrightarrow \neg p$	$p \Longrightarrow q$
1	1	0	0	1	1
1	0	1	0	0	0
0	1	0	1	1	1
0	0	1	1	1	1

$$p \wedge (q \vee r) \equiv (p \wedge q) \vee (p \wedge r)$$

p	q	r	$q \vee r$	$p \wedge (q \vee r)$	$p \wedge q$	$p \wedge r$	$(p \wedge q) \vee (p \wedge r)$
1	1	1	1	1	1	1	1
1	1	0	1	1	1	0	1
1	0	1	1	1	0	1	1
1	0	0	0	0	0	0	0
0	1	1	1	0	0	0	0
0	1	0	1	0	0	0	0
0	0	1	1	0	0	0	0
0	0	0	0	0	0	0	0

Using truth tables, prove each of the following equivalences.

a) $p \Longrightarrow q \quad \equiv \neg p \vee q$

b) $p \Longrightarrow q \quad \equiv \neg (p \wedge \neg q)$

c) $p \vee q \quad \equiv \neg (\neg p \wedge \neg q)$

d) $p \Longrightarrow q \quad \equiv \neg q \Longrightarrow \neg p$

e) $p \Longrightarrow q \quad \equiv (p \wedge \neg q) \Longrightarrow \neg p$

f) $p \Longrightarrow q \quad \equiv (p \wedge \neg q) \Longrightarrow q$

g) $p \Longrightarrow q \quad \equiv (p \wedge \neg q) \Longrightarrow (r \wedge \neg r)$

h) $p \Longleftrightarrow q \quad \equiv (p \Longrightarrow q) \wedge (q \Longrightarrow p)$

i) $p \wedge q \quad \equiv q \wedge p$

j) $p \vee q \quad \equiv q \vee p$

k) $p \wedge (q \quad r) \equiv (p \wedge q) \vee (p \wedge r)$

l) $p \vee (q \wedge r) \equiv (p \vee q) \wedge (p \vee r)$

m) $p \quad \equiv \neg (\neg p)$

n) $p \wedge (q \wedge r) \equiv (p \wedge q) \wedge r$

o) $(p \vee q) \vee r \equiv p \vee (q \vee r)$

p) $p \wedge p \quad \equiv p$

q) $p \vee p \quad \equiv p$

This exercise suggests how logic is formalized. The student interested in pursuing the subject should consult one of the texts on logic suggested in the reference list.

1.2 The quantifiers $\forall$ and $\exists$ are related as follows: $\forall x: p$ is equivalent to $\neg (\exists x: \neg p)$, or in words, (for all x, p is true) is equivalent to (it is not the case that there exists an x such that p is false). ALSO TRUE IF ROLES ARE REVERSED!

Prove this equivalence: $\neg (\forall x)$: $(x \in X \Longrightarrow x \in Y)$ is equivalent to $(\exists x)$: $(x \in X \wedge x \notin Y)$. Write out a statement of this theorem using the word *subset*.

1.3 Prove that equality for sets is reflexive, symmetric, and transitive; that is, prove these theorems:

a) $X = X$ for all sets X.

b) If $X = Y$, then $Y = X$ for all sets X, Y.

c) For all sets, X, Y, Z, if $X = Y$ and $Y = Z$, then $X = Z$.

1.4 Prove that inclusion for sets is reflexive, antisymmetric, and transitive; that is, prove these theorems:

a) $X \subset X$ for all sets X.

b) $X \subset Y$ and $Y \subset X$ imply $X = Y$ for all sets X, Y.

c) For all sets, X, Y, Z if $X \subset Y$ and $Y \subset Z$ then $X \subset Z$.

1.5 Let $A \subsetneqq B$ and $B \subsetneqq C$. Prove that $A \subsetneqq C$.

1.6 Let $A \subset B$ and $B \subset C$ and $C \subset A$. Prove that $A = B = C$.

1.7 Let $P \subset U$ and $Q \subset U$. Define $P' = \{x | x \in U \text{ and } x \notin P\}$ and Q' similarly. Prove that $P \subset Q$ iff $Q' \subset P'$. Prove furthermore that $P = (P')'$. Note: *iff* is an abbreviation for *if and only if.*

1.8 Prove that $\emptyset \subset P$. Prove that $P \subset \emptyset$ iff $P = \emptyset$.

1.9 By definition
$$P \cup Q = \{x | x \in P \text{ or } x \in Q\} = \bigcup\{P, Q\}$$
$$P \cap Q = \{x | x \in P \text{ and } x \in Q\} = \bigcap\{P, Q\}.$$
If P and Q are sets, then prove that $P \cup Q$ and $P \cap Q$ are sets.

1.10 Prove that $\emptyset$ is a neutral element for the union of sets, i.e., that $X \cup \emptyset = \emptyset \cup X = X$ for all sets X.

1.11 Let $X \cup Y = X$ for all sets X. Prove that $Y = \emptyset$.

1.12 Prove that $X \cap \emptyset = \emptyset$ for all sets X.

1.13 Prove the following theorems:

a) The commutativity of union, $P \cup Q = Q \cup P$.

b) The commutativity of intersection, $P \cap Q = Q \cap P$
c) The associativity of union, $P \cup (Q \cup R) = (P \cup Q) \cup R$.
d) The associativity of intersection, $P \cap (Q \cap R) = (P \cap Q) \cap R$
e) The distributivity of intersection with respect to union, $P \cap (Q \cup R) = (P \cap Q) \cup (P \cap R)$.
f) The distributivity of union with respect to intersection, $P \cup (Q \cap R) = (P \cup Q) \cap (P \cup R)$.
g) The idempotency of union, $P \cup P = P$.
h) The idempotency of intersection, $P \cap P = P$.

1.14 Define $0 = \emptyset$, $1 = 0 \cup \{0\}$, $2 = 1 \cup \{1\}$, $3 = 2 \cup \{2\}$, $4 = 3 \cup \{3\}$. Prove that 0, 1, 2, 3, 4 are sets. These sets which are denoted by the symbols used for the nonnegative integers will show up frequently in these exercises.

1.15 Express the set 4 using only the symbols $\{$, $\}$, $\emptyset$, , .

1.16 Prove each of these statements true or false:

a) $1 \in 2$
b) $1 \subset 2$
c) $1 \cap 2 = 0$
d) $1 \cup 2 = 2$
e) $(0 \cap 2) \in 1$.

1.17 In order to generalize the construction of 1.14, assume an intuitive knowledge of the natural numbers (nonnegative whole numbers) and proof by mathematical induction. For each natural number n define a set S_n as follows: $S_0 = \emptyset$, $S_{n+1} = S_n \cup \{S_n\}$. Prove that S_0 is a set. Prove that if S_n is a set, then S_{n+1} is a set. Conclude that S_n is a set for each natural number n. Finally, identify n and S_n; that is, use the symbol n to denote the natural number as intuitively understood and the constructed set. These sets, 0, 1, 2, 3,... will be used in succeeding exercises.

1.18 Of which of the following sets is x a member, x a subset, x neither a member nor a subset?

A) $\{\{x\}, y\}$ D) $\{x\} - \{\{x\}\}$

B) x E) $\{x\} \cup x$

C) $\emptyset \cap x$ F) $\{x\} \cup \{\emptyset\}$.

1.19 Show that

a) $\bigcup \{\{a, b, c\}, \{a, d, e\}, \{a, f\}\} = \{a, b, c, d, e, f\}$

b) $\bigcap \{\{a, b, c\}, \{a, d, e\}, \{a, f\}\} = \{a\}$

c) $\bigcup \{1\} = 1$

d) $\bigcap \{1\} = 1$

e) $\bigcup \{A\} = A$ for all sets A

f) $\bigcap \{A\} = A$ for all sets A.

1.20 Express the following sets using the sets 0, 1, 2, etc. $\emptyset$, $\bigcup\emptyset$, $\mathcal{P}\emptyset$, $\bigcup\bigcup\emptyset$, $\mathcal{P}\mathcal{P}\emptyset$, $\bigcup\bigcup\bigcup\emptyset$, $\mathcal{P}\mathcal{P}\mathcal{P}\emptyset$.

1.21 Let $X = \{\{2, 5\}, 4, \{4\}\}$. Find $\bigcap(\bigcup X - 4)$.

1.22 Construct $(\bigcup \mathcal{P} 1)'$ where $A' = 3 - A$ for any set A.

1.23 Construct $\bigcap \bigcup (\mathcal{P} 2 - 2)$.

1.24 Let $X = \{\{\{1, 2\}, \{1\}\}, \{\{1, 0\}\}\}$. Construct $\bigcup X$, $\bigcap X$, $\bigcup\bigcup X$, $\bigcap\bigcap X$, $\bigcup\bigcap X$, $\bigcap\bigcup X$.

1.25 Let $X = \{\{1, 2\}, \{2, 0\}, \{1, 3\}\}$. Construct $\bigcup X$, $\bigcap X$, $\bigcup\bigcup X$, $\bigcap\bigcap X$, $\bigcup\bigcap X$, $\bigcap\bigcup X$.

1.26 Let P, Q, R be subsets of U and let the relative complements ($'$) be with respect to U. Then prove the following:

a) $P \subset Q$ iff $P \cap Q' = \emptyset$

b) $P \subset Q$ iff $P' \cup Q = U$

c) $P \subset Q$ iff $(P \cap Q') \subset P'$

d) $P \subset Q$ iff $(P \cap Q') \subset Q$

e) $P \subset Q$ iff $(P \cap Q') \subset (R \cap R')$.

1.27 Prove that $A \cup B = A$ iff $B \subset A$.

1.28 Prove that $A \cap B = A$ iff $A \subset B$.

1.29 Give an example of two sets A, B such that $(\bigcap A) \cap (\bigcap B) \neq \bigcap(A \cap B)$.

1.30 Prove that $(\bigcap A) \cap (\bigcap B) \subset \bigcap(A \cap B)$.

1.31 Give an example of two sets A, B such that $\mathcal{P}(A \cap B) \neq (\mathcal{P} A) \cup (\mathcal{P} B)$.

1.32 Assuming a knowledge of **R**, the real numbers, what subset is described here? $\{x|\, x^2 > 2\} \cap \{x|\, |x-2| < |x+3|\}$.

1.33 Define $A + B = (A-B) \cup (B-A)$ to be the symmetric difference of the sets A and B. Prove the following:

a) $A + \emptyset = A$

b) $A + B = B + A$

c) $A + (B+C) = (A+B) + C$

d) $A \cap (B+C) = (A \cap B) + (A \cap C)$

e) $A - B \subset A + B$

f) $A = B$ iff $A + B = \emptyset$

g) $A + C = B + C$ implies $A = B$.

1.34 Prove that $\{A\}$ is a set without using the axiom of pairing.

CHAPTER 2

THE ORDERED PAIR AND THE CARTESIAN PRODUCT

2.0 Definition of Ordered Pair. $(a, b) = \{\{a\}, \{a, b\}\}$. (NST p23)

Definition of Cartesian Product. $A \times B = \{x \mid x = (a, b)$ for some $a \in A$ and some $b \in B\}$. (NST p24)

2.1 Construct these sets:

a) $2 \cup 3$ d) 2×1 g) 1×1 .

b) $2 \cap 3$ e) 1×2

c) 2×3 f) 0×1

2.2 Show that $\{x, y\}$ cannot serve as the definition for an ordered pair; show that it does not have the property $(x, y) = (a, b)$ iff $x = a$ and $y = b$.

2.3 An ordered pair is by definition a set. Show by example that not every ordered pair has two members.

2.4 Prove this proposition false: $X \times Y = Y \times X$ for all sets X, Y. The Cartesian product is not commutative.

2.5 Prove that the Cartesian product is nonassociative.

2.6 Give an example of two sets X, Y such that $X \times Y = Y \times X$.

2.7 Prove that the Cartesian product is distributive with respect to union: $X \times (Y \cup Z) = (X \times Y) \cup (X \times Z)$ for all X, Y, Z.

2.8 Give examples of sets such that $X \cup (Y \times Z) \neq (X \cup Y) \times (X \cup Z)$.

2.9 Prove that $\bigcap\bigcap(x, y) = x$.

2.10 Prove $[\bigcap\bigcup(x, y)] \cup [\bigcup\bigcup(x, y) - \bigcup\bigcap(x, y)] = y$.

2.11 Prove that $X \times X = Y \times Y$ implies $X = Y$.

2.12 Prove that $X \times Y = X \times Z$ and $X \neq \emptyset$ imply $Y = Z$.

CHAPTER 3

RELATIONS

3.0 Definition of a Relation from X to Y. R is a relation from X to Y iff $R \subset X \times Y$. One writes $x R y$ if $(x, y) \in R$.

Definition of the Image of a Relation. Image $R = \{y | (x, y) \in R$ for some $x \in X\}$.

Definition of the preimage of a Relation. Preimage $R = \{x | (x, y) \in R$ for some $y \in Y\}$.

Definition. A relation R on X (from X to X) is

a) reflexive iff for all $x \in X$, $(x, x) \in R$

b) irreflexive iff for all $x \in X$, $(x, x) \notin R$

c) transitive iff $(x, y) \in R$ and $(y, z) \in R$ imply $(x, z) \in R$

d) atransitive iff $(x, y) \in R$ and $(y, z) \in R$ imply $(x, z) \notin R$

e) symmetric iff $(x, y) \in R$ implies $(y, x) \in R$

f) antisymmetric iff $(x, y) \in R$ and $(y, x) \in R$ imply $x = y$. (NST p27)

Definition of Composition. If R is a relation from X to Y and S is a relation from Y to Z then $S \circ R = \{(x, z) | (x, y) \in R$ and $(y, z) \in S$ for some $y \in Y\}$. (NST p41)

Definition of Inverse Relation. If R is a relation from X to Y then $R^{-1} = \{(y, x) | (x, y) \in R\}$. (NST p40)

Definition. An equivalence relation on X is a reflexive, symmetric, transitive relation on X. (NST p27)

Definition. An order on X is a reflexive, antisymmetric, transitive relation. (NST p54)

Definition. A strict order on X is an irreflexive, antisymmetric, transitive relation on X. (NST p54)

Definition. An order R on X is total iff $x, y \in X$ imply $(x, y) \in R$ or $(y, x) \in R$. (NST p54)

Definition of Partition. P is a partition of X iff $P \subset \mathcal{P}X$, $X = \bigcup P$, $\emptyset \notin P$ and $A, B \in P$ imply $A \cap B = \emptyset$ or $A = B$.

Theorem. Associated with an equivalence relation R on a set X is a partition $X/R = \{x/R \mid x \in X\}$ in which $x/R = \{y \mid y \in X \text{ and } (x, y) \in R\}$. (NST p28)

3.1 List all the relations from $X = \{a, b, c\}$ to $Y = \{s\}$.

3.2 List all the relations on the set 1.

3.3 How many relations are there on a set with n elements?

3.4 Let R be a relation from W to X, S a relation from X to Y, and T a relation from Y to Z. Prove the associativity of the composite: $T \circ (S \circ R) = (T \circ S) \circ R$.

3.5 Let S be a relation from X to Y. Prove that S^{-1} is a relation from Y to X.

3.6 Define $I_X = \{(x, y) \mid (x, y) \in X \times X \text{ and } x = y\}$. Let S be a relation from X to Y. Prove that $I_Y \cdot S = S$ and $S \cdot I_X = S$.

3.7 Let S be a relation from X to Y and T a relation from Y to Z. Define for $A \subset X$, $S(A) = \{y \mid (x, y) \in S \text{ for some } x \in A\}$. Prove that $S(A) \subset Y$. Prove that $(T \circ S)(A) = T(S(A))$. Prove that $S(A \cup B) = S(A) \cup S(B)$. Prove that $S(A \cap B) \subset S(A) \cap S(B)$.

3.8 Let S and T be relations from X to Y. Then prove $(S \cap T)^{-1} = S^{-1} \cap T^{-1}$, $(S \cup T)^{-1} = S^{-1} \cup T^{-1}$.

3.9 Let S be a relation from X to Y and T a relation from Y to Z. Then prove $(T \circ S)^{-1} = S^{-1} \circ T^{-1}$.

3.10 Prove that for a relation S on X

S is reflexive	iff	$I_X \subset S$
S is irreflexive	iff	$I_X \cap S = \emptyset$
S is transitive	iff	$(S \circ S) \subset S$
S is atransitive	iff	$(S \circ S) \cap S = \emptyset$
S is symmetric	iff	$S = S^{-1}$
S is antisymmetric	iff	$S \cap S^{-1} \subset I_X$

3.11 Let S be a relation on X. Prove that if S is transitive and reflexive, then $S \circ S = S$. Is the converse true?

3.12 Construct all equivalence relations on the set 3.

3.13 Let $\mathcal{S}$ be a nonempty set of equivalence relations on a set X. Prove that $\bigcap \mathcal{S}$ is an equivalence relation on X.

3.14 Let X be a set. Verify that equality of sets is an equivalence relation on $\mathcal{P} X$.

3.15 Construct all orders on the set 3. Which are total?

3.16 Can $\emptyset$ be an equivalence relation? An order?

3.17 Let $\mathcal{S}$ be a nonempty set of orders on a set X. Prove that $\bigcap \mathcal{S}$ is an order.

3.18 Verify that inclusion is an order on X.

3.19 If S is an order on a set X and $A \subset X$, prove that $S \cap (A \times A)$ is an order on A. Prove that if S is total on X, then $S \cap (A \times A)$ is total on A.

3.20 Prove that S^{-1} is an order on X iff S is an order on X.

3.21 Construct the following relations on the set 8, relying upon your previous knowledge of arithmetic. The symbol (–) in this exercise means arithmetic difference and not relative complement.

a) $\leq$, where $x \leq y$ iff $y - x \in 8$
b) $<$, where $x < y$ iff $y - x \in 8$ and $y - x \neq 0$
c) $=$, where $x = y$ iff $y - x = 0$
d) $\sim$, where $x \sim y$ iff $y - x$ an integer divisible by 2
e) $*$, where $x * y$ iff $4 < x - y$
f) s, where $x \, s \, y$ iff $y - x = 1$

Which relations are symmetric? antisymmetric? reflexive? irreflexive? transitive? atransitive? Which relations are orders? equivalence relations? For each equivalence relation what is the corresponding partition of 8?

3.22 Let L be the set of all lines of the Euclidean plane. Verify that parallelism is an equivalence relation on L. Verify that perpendicularity is an irreflexive, symmetric, atransitive relation.

3.23 Let $\mathbf{Q}$ be the set of rational numbers. By $\mathbf{Q}[X]$ is meant the set of all polynomials in X with rational coefficients. Define a relation on $A = \mathbf{Q}[X] - \mathbf{Q}$ as follows: for all $f, g \in A$, $f \prec g$ iff $g = qf$ for some $q \in A$. Prove that $\prec$ is a strict order on A. Is $(\prec) \cup I$ total?

3.24 If S is an order on X, prove that $S - I_X$ is a strict order. If S is a strict order on X, prove that $S \cup I_X$ is an order.

3.25 Can $\emptyset$ be a strict order?

3.26 Let S be a relation on X. Prove that S is a relation on $\bigcup\bigcup S$. Prove that $\bigcup\bigcup S \subset X$.

3.27 Let S be a relation from X to Y. Prove that preimage $S \subset X$ and image $S \subset Y$.

3.28 Let S be a relation from X to Y. Prove that $I_{\text{preimage } S} \subset S^{-1} \circ S$. Prove that $I_{\text{image } S} \subset S \circ S^{-1}$.

3.29 Let S be an order on X and T an order on Y. Let $((x_1, y_1), (x_2, y_2)) \in P$ iff $(x_1, x_2) \in S$ and $(y_1, y_2) \in T$. Prove that P is an order on $X \times Y$ (the product order).

3.30 Let S be an equivalence relation on X and T an equivalence relation on Y. Let $((x_1, y_1), (x_2, y_2)) \in P$ iff $(x_1, x_2) \in S$ and $(y_1, y_2) \in T$. Prove that P is an equivalence relation on $X \times Y$.

3.31 Let S be a strict order on X and T be a strict order on Y. On $X \times Y$ define a relation R as follows: $((x_1, y_1), (y_2, y_2)) \in R$ iff $(y_1, y_2) \in T$ or $[(x_1, x_2) \in S$ and $y_1 = y_2]$. R is said to be an ordering by last differences. Prove R is a strict order on $X \times Y$.

3.32 Let S and T be partitions of X. S is finer than T iff $u \in S$ implies $u \subset v$ for some $v \in T$. Prove that the relation *is finer than* is an order on the set of all partitions of X.

3.33 Give an example of a set X and a set $\mathcal{S}$ of orders on X such that $\bigcup \mathcal{S}$ is not an order on X.

3.34 Let R be a relation on X. Prove that $R \cup R^{-1}$ is the smallest symmetric relation including R and that $R \cap R^{-1}$ is the largest symmetric relation included in R.

3.35 Let R be a relation on X such that R is reflexive and transitive. R is not necessarily an order because R is not necessarily antisymmetric. Prove that there exist an equivalence relations on X and an order $\overline{R}$ on X/S such that $(x/S, y/S) \in \overline{R}$ iff $(x, y) \in R$.

CHAPTER 4

FUNCTIONS

4.0 Definition. f is a function from X to Y iff $f \subset X \times Y$, for all $x \in X$ there is a $y \in Y$ such that $(x, y) \in f$, $(x, y_1) \in f$, and $(x, y_2) \in f$ imply $y_1 = y_2$.

Also by definition,

$f: X \to Y$ means f is a function from X to Y,
domain $f = X$, range $f = Y$,
image $f = \{y \mid y \in Y \text{ and } (x, y) \in f \text{ for some } x \in X\}$,
$y = f(x)$ means $(x, y) \in f$,
y is the image of x under f means $(x, y) \in f$,
x is the preimage of y under f means $(x, y) \in f$,
y is the value of the function f at x means $(x, y) \in f$.

Definition. A function f from X to Y is a surjection (also called an onto function) iff for all $y \in Y$ there exists an $x \in X$ such that $(x, y) \in f$.

$f: X \longrightarrow\!\!\!\!\!\to Y$ means f is a surjection from X to Y.

Definition. A function f from X to Y is an injection (also called a one-to-one function) iff $(x_1, y) \in f$ and $(x_2, y) \in f$ imply $x_1 = x_2$.

$f: X \rightarrowtail Y$ means f is an injection from X to Y.

Definition. A function f from X to Y is a bijection iff f is both an injection and a surjection.

$f: X \rightarrowtail\!\!\!\!\!\to Y$ means f is a bijection from X to Y.

A bijection is also called an equivalence. In case there is an $f\colon X \rightarrowtail\twoheadrightarrow Y$, one calls the sets X and Y equivalent: $X \sim Y$.

Definition. $Y^X = \{f \mid f\colon X \to Y\}$. (NST p30)

Definition. Let $f\colon A \to Y$, $g\colon B \to Y$ and $g \subset f$. Then g is a restriction of f and f is an extension of g.
$(f|B) = f \cap (B \times Y) = g$. (NST p32)

Definition of Quotient Map. If X/R is a partition of X, then the surjection $\phi\colon X \twoheadrightarrow X/R$ such that $\phi(x) = x/R$ is called the quotient map (or canonical map). (NST p32)

Definition of Characteristic Function. If A is a subset of a set X, the characteristic function of A is the function $\chi_A\colon X \to 2$ such that $\chi_A(x) = 1$ for $x \in A$ and $\chi_A(x) = 0$ for $x \notin A$. (NST p33)

Definition of a Monoid. A monoid is an ordered pair (A, w) in which A is a set and w is an associative operation on A with a neutral element e.
An operation on a set A is a function w from $A \times A$ to A. Writing $x\,w\,y$ for the operation value $w(x, y)$, e is a neutral element for the operation w iff $e\,w\,x = x\,w\,e = x$ for all $x \in A$.

Definition of a Submonoid. Let (A, w) be a monoid. A subset S of A is a submonoid of A iff $x, y \in S$ imply $xy \in S$ and $yx \in S$ and $e \in S$. By abuse of language (G, w) *is a monoid* is usually written G *is a monoid.*

Definition of a Semigroup. A left semigroup is a monoid (A, w) with a left cancellation law, i.e., $x\,w\,y = x\,w\,z$ implies $y = z$.

Definition of a Group. A monoid (G, w) is a group iff every element of G is invertible. x is an invertible element of G iff $x\,w\,y = y\,w\,x = e$ for some $y \in G$.

Students who do not find these definitions sufficient to work the problems on algebra can consult references 18, 19, 20.

4.1 Let **N** represent the nonnegative integers, **Z** the integers, **Q** the rational numbers and **R** the real numbers. Assuming an acquaintance with these sets, give an example of a function:

a) from **N** to a proper subset of **N**, and not an injection,
b) which is an injection from **N** to a proper subset of **N**,
c) from **Z** to a proper subset of **Z** and not an injection,
d) which is an injection from **Z** to a proper subset of **Z**,
e) from **R** to **N**,
f) from **R** to **N** such that for all x, $f(x) \neq x$.

4.2 Prove that not every injection of a set into itself is a bijection.

4.3 Construct a function a) from 1 to 1, b) from 0 to 1, c) from 2×3 to 6, from 6 to 2×3, both bijections.

4.4 Construct these sets

a) 2^3	c) 2^0	e) 0^0	g) 1^1	i) 2^1
b) 3^2	d) 0^2	f) 1^0	h) 0^1	j) 1^2 .

4.5 Let there exist a function from X to Y which is not an injection. Prove that $X \neq \emptyset$ and $Y \neq \emptyset$.

4.6 Let there exist a function from X to Y which is not a surjection. Prove that $Y \neq \emptyset$.

4.7 Prove that $\mathcal{P}\mathcal{P}\mathcal{P}\emptyset \sim 4$. $\sim$ means equivalent.

4.8 Prove that $A^B = 0$ iff $A = 0$ and $B \neq 0$.

4.9 $X^Y = Y^X$ implies $X = Y$. Prove.

4.10 Prove that if $A \subset B$, then $A^C \subset B^C$.

4.11 Prove that if $A \quad B$, then $A^C \sim B^C$.

4.12 Let $f: X \to X$. Prove that if $f \subset I_X$, then $f = I_X$.

4.13 Let $f\colon X \to X$. Prove that if $I_X \subset f$, then $f = I_X$.

4.14 Let $f\colon X \to X$. Let n be a positive integer such that $f^n = I_X$. ($f^{n+1} = f \circ f^n$.) Prove that f is a bijection.

4.15 Let A, B, C be sets such that $B \cap C = \emptyset$. Prove that $A^{B \cup C} \sim A^B \times A^C$.

4.16 Is $(A^B)^C \sim A^{B \times C}$?

4.17 Prove that $(A \times B)^C \sim A^C \times B^C$.

4.18 Prove that if $\overline{\mathfrak{R}}$ is the set of all orders on a set X and $\mathfrak{R}$ is the set of all strict orders on X, then there exists a bijection $\Phi\colon \mathfrak{R} \rightarrowtail\!\!\twoheadrightarrow \overline{\mathfrak{R}}$.

4.19 Prove that there is a set $\mathcal{E}$ of all equivalence relations on a set X and a set $\mathcal{F}$ of all partitions of a set X. Prove that there exists a bijection $\Phi\colon \mathcal{E} \rightarrowtail\!\!\twoheadrightarrow \mathcal{F}$.

4.20 Let P and Q be partitions of X. Define the cross partition of P and Q to be $P \dagger Q = \{A \cap B \mid A \in P \text{ and } B \in Q\} - \{\emptyset\}$. Prove that $P \dagger Q$ is finer than both P and Q and, furthermore, is the least fine partition finer than both P and Q: $P \dagger Q = \sup\{P, Q\}$. (Cf. 3.32.) Let R, S be the equivalence relations naturally corresponding respectively to P and Q. Prove that $R \cap S$ corresponds to $P \dagger Q$. Prove there exists a partition which is $\inf\{P, Q\}$.

4.21 Let $X \neq \emptyset$. Define $f\,S\,g$ iff image f = image g for f, $g \in X^X$. Prove that S is an equivalence relation on X^X and that $X^X/S \sim \mathcal{P}X - 1$.

4.22 Assume a knowledge of the real numbers, $\mathbf{R}$. Let $X = \mathbf{R}^{[0,1]}$. Let $f, g \in X$. Define $(f, g) \in S$ iff $f(x) - g(x) \geq 0$ for all $x \in [0, 1]$. Prove that S is an order. Is the order total?

4.23 Let $\chi_A\colon X \to 2$ be the characteristic function of X defined by the subset A of X. Prove $\Phi\colon \mathcal{P}X \rightarrowtail\!\!\twoheadrightarrow 2^X$ where $\Phi(A) = \chi_A$ for $A \subset X$.

4.24 Construct χ_2 where $\chi_2 \in 2^3$.

4.25 Let $f: X \to Y$, $g: X \to Y$. Let $A = \{x | x \in X \text{ and } f(x) = g(x)\}$ and let $i: A >\!\!\longrightarrow X$ be the identity injection. Show that $f \circ i = g \circ i$. Let B be any other subset of X with $j: B >\!\!\longrightarrow X$ the identity injection from B such that $f \circ j = g \circ j$. Prove that $B \subset A$.

4.26 Let $f: X \to Y$ and $g: X \to Y$. Prove that there exists an equivalence relation R on Y such that if $\phi_R: Y \longrightarrow\!\!\!\!\!\rightarrow Y/R$ is the associated quotient map, then $\phi_R \circ g = \phi_R \circ f$, and moreover, if T is any other equivalence relation on Y such that $\phi_T \circ f = \phi_T \circ g$, then $R \subset T$, Y/R is finer than Y/T. Hence there exists a $t: Y/R \longrightarrow\!\!\!\!\!\rightarrow Y/T$ such that $t \circ \phi_R = \phi_T$.

4.27 Let $f: X \to Y$ and $g: Y \to X$. Let $g \circ f$ be the identity on X. Prove that f is an injection and g is a surjection.

4.28 Let $f: X \to Y$ and $g: Y \to X$. Let $g \circ f$ be the identity on X and $f \circ g$ be the identity on Y. Prove f and g are bijections and $g = f^{-1}$.

4.29 Let $h \in X^X$. Prove that if $h \circ f = h \circ g$, then $f = g$ for all $f, g \in X^X$ iff h is an injection.

4.30 Let $h \in X^X$. Prove that if $f \circ h = g \circ h$, then $f = g$ for all $f, g \in X^X$ iff h is a surjection.

4.31 Let X be a set. Prove that X^X together with functional composition is a monoid.

4.32 Prove that $\mathfrak{I}$, the set of injections of X, constitutes a submonoid of $(X^X, \circ)$ and that this submonoid is a left semigroup.

4.33 Prove that $\mathcal{S}$, the set of surjections of X, constitutes a submonoid of $(X^X, \circ)$ and that this submonoid is a right semigroup.

4.34 Let $\mathfrak{S} = \mathfrak{I} \cap \mathcal{S}$. Prove that $\mathfrak{S}$ is a submonoid of $(X^X, \circ)$ and, moreover, is a group. It is called the symmetric group of X.

4.35 Let $f \in \mathfrak{S}$. Prove that f is a reflexive relation iff $f = I_X$, the identity of $\mathfrak{S}$.

4.36 Let $f \in \mathfrak{S}$. Prove that f is a transitive relation iff f is an idempotent element of $\mathfrak{S}$; i.e., $f^2 = f$.

4.37 Let $f \in \mathfrak{S}$. Prove that f is a symmetric relation iff $f^2 = I_X$.

CHAPTER 5

FAMILIES

5.0 Definition of a Family. A family $(X_i)_{i \in I}$ is a function with domain I and value X_i for each $i \in I$. (NST p34)

Definition of the Union of a Family $(X_i)_{i \in I}$.

$$\bigcup_{i \in I} X_i = \bigcup \text{image } (X_i)_{i \in I} = \{x \mid x \in X_i \text{ for some } i \in I\}.$$

(NST p34)

Definition of the Intersection of a Family $(X_i)_{i \in I}$, $I \neq \emptyset$.

$$\bigcap_{i \in I} X_i = \bigcap \text{image } (X_i)_{i \in I} = \{x \mid x \in X_i \text{ for all } i \in I\},\ I \neq \emptyset.$$

(NST p34)

Definition of the Cartesian Product of a Family $(X_i)_{i \in I}$.

$$\mathsf{X}_{i \in I} X_i = \{(x_i)_{i \in I} \mid x_i \in X_i\}.$$ (NST p36)

Definition of Projection Function. Let $(X_i)_{i \in I}$, $J \subset I$ be given. Then define,

$\text{proj}_J \colon \mathsf{X}_{i \in I} X_i \twoheadrightarrow \mathsf{X}_{i \in J} X_i$ such that

$\text{proj}_J\, (x_i)_{i \in I} = (x_i)_{i \in J}$. (NST p36)

5.1 Let $X_0 = \{a, b\}$, $X_1 = \{A\}$, $X_2 = \{\alpha, \beta, \gamma\}$, $I = 3$. Construct $(X_i)_{i \in I}$ and $\mathsf{X}_{i \in I} X_i$.

5.2 Let $I = 3$, $X_i = i$ for all $i \in 3$. Construct $(X_i)_{i \in I}$ and $\mathsf{X}_{i \in I} X_i$.

5.3 Let $I = 3$, $X_0 = 1$, $X_1 = 2$, $X_3 = 3$. Construct $(X_i)_{i \in I}$ and $\mathsf{X}_{i \in I} X_i$.

5.4 Prove that $X_0 \times X_1 \sim \underset{i \in 2}{\mathsf{X}} X_i$.

5.5 Let $X_2 \neq \emptyset$. Prove that there exists an injection from $X_0 \times X_1$ to $\underset{i \in 3}{\mathsf{X}} X_i$. Does the injection still exist if $X_2 = \emptyset$?

5.6 Prove that there exists an injection from $X \times \underset{i \in I}{\mathsf{X}} X_i$ to $\underset{i \in I}{\mathsf{X}} (X \times X_i)$. Is there a bijection?

5.7 Let $\{I_j \mid j \in J\}$ be a partition of a set I. Then prove

$$\underset{i \in I}{\mathsf{X}} X_i \sim \underset{j \in J}{\mathsf{X}} (\underset{i \in I_j}{\mathsf{X}} X_i) .$$

5.8 Is it the case that

$$(\underset{i \in I}{\mathsf{X}} X_i)^Y \sim \underset{i \in I}{\mathsf{X}} (X_i{}^Y) \; ?$$

5.9 Let families $(X_i)_{i \in I}$, $(Y_j)_{j \in J}$ be given. Prove that

$$(\bigcup_{i \in I} X_i) \times (\bigcup_{j \in J} Y_j) = \bigcup_{(i,j) \in I \times J} (X_i \times Y_j) .$$

5.10 Let F be the set of all real valued functions defined on the unit interval $[0, 1]$. Express F as an exponential set and also express F as a Cartesian product.

5.11 For a set X let $(X_i)_{i \in I}$ be the family of all subsets of X indexed by itself; viz., $I = \mathcal{P} X - 1$ and $X_i = i$. $\underset{i \in I}{\mathsf{X}} X_i$ is called the set of all choice functions for X. Is the name appropriate?

5.12 Prove that $\underset{i \in \mathbf{N}}{\mathsf{X}} \mathbf{R}^{[i, i+1)} \sim \mathbf{R}^{\mathbf{R}}$.

5.13 Let $(X_i)_{i \in 3}$ be given with $X_i = \mathbf{R}$ for each $i \in 3$. Find each of the following sets and interpret geometrically in Euclidean 3-space.

$$\text{proj}_{\{0,1\}} \{(x_i)_{i \in 3} \mid ax_0 + bx_1 + cx_2 = 1 \text{ with } |a| + |b| + |c| \neq 0\} .$$

$$\text{proj}_{\{0,1\}} \{(x_i)_{i \in 3} \mid \sum_{i \in 3} x_i^2 = 1\} .$$

CHAPTER 6

FUNCTIONS DEFINED ON POWER SETS

6.0 Definition. Given $f\colon X \to Y$ define
$\overline{f}\colon \mathcal{P}X \to \mathcal{P}Y$ such that $\overline{f}(A) = \{y \mid (x, y) \in f$ for some $x \in A\}$
$\overline{f}^{-1}\colon \mathcal{P}Y \to \mathcal{P}X$ such that $\overline{f}^{-1}(B) = \{x \mid (x, y) \in f$ for some $y \in B\}$.

6.1 Let $f\colon X \to Y$. Prove that $\overline{f}^{-1}$ is surjective iff f is injective.

6.2 Let $f\colon X \to Y$. Prove that $\overline{f}^{-1}$ is injective iff f is surjective.

6.3 Let $f\colon X \to Y$. Prove that f is injective iff the inverse image under f of each singleton in the image of f is a singleton in the domain of f. (NST p38)

6.4 Let $f\colon X \to Y$. Prove that f is surjective iff the inverse image under f of each nonempty subset of Y is a nonempty subset of X. (NST p38)

6.5 Supply in a nontrivial way the missing hypothesis for this theorem. If $f\colon X \to Y$ and $(A_i)_{i \in I}$ is a family with $A_i \in \mathcal{P}X$ for every $i \in I$, then

$$\overline{f}\Big(\bigcap_{i \in I} A_i\Big) = \bigcap_{i \in I} \overline{f}(A_i) .$$

6.6 Let $f\colon X \to Y$. Is it the case that $\overline{f}^{-1}(A-B) = \overline{f}^{-1}(A) - \overline{f}^{-1}(B)$ for all $A, B \in \mathcal{P}Y$?

6.7 Let $f: X \to Y$. Is it the case that $\overline{f}(A-B) \subset \overline{f}(A) - \overline{f}(B)$ for all $A, B \in \mathcal{P}X$? Is it the case that $\overline{f}(A) - \overline{f}(B) \subset \overline{f}(A-B)$ for all $A, B \in \mathcal{P}X$?

6.8 Let $f: X \to Y$. Let $A_i \in \mathcal{P}X$ for each $i \in I$. Prove that

$$\overline{f}\left(\bigcap_{i \in I} A_i\right) \subset \bigcap_{i \in I} \overline{f}(A_i) .$$

Give a counter example for

$$\bigcap_{i \in I} \overline{f}(A_i) \subset \overline{f}\left(\bigcap_{i \in I} A_i\right) .$$

6.9 Let $f(x, y) = x^2 + y^2$ for all real numbers x, y.

a) What is domain f?

b) What is range f?

c) What is image f?

d) $\overline{f}^{-1}([0, 1]) = ?$ $[0, 1]$ is the closed unit interval of R.

e) Is f injective or surjective?

f) If $A = \{(x, y) \mid x+y = \sqrt{2}\}$, then $f(A) = ?$

CHAPTER 7

APPLICATIONS OF FUNCTIONS

7.0 Definition. Let G with an operation $w: G \times G \to G$ be a group. Represent the operation w by multiplication: if $x, y \in G$, then $w(x, y) = xy$. Let $S \subset G$, $a \in G$. Then by definition $aS = \{ax | x \in S\}$ and $Sa = \{xa | x \in S\}$. A subset N of G is a normal subgroup of G iff N is a subgroup of G and $x^{-1}Nx = N$ for all $x \in G$.

A commutative group (monoid) G is a group G (monoid) in which the operation is commutative; $xy = yx$ for all $x, y \in G$. Let G and H be groups (monoids) with the operations of both expressed multiplicatively. $f: G \to H$ is a homomorphism iff $f(xy) = f(x)f(y)$ for all $x, y \in G$ and $f(e_G) = e_H$. kernel $f = \bar{f}^{-1}(e_H)$.

Definitions. $(R, +, \cdot)$, a commutative ring with identity, is a set together with two operations (here represented by $+$ and $\cdot$) such that $(R, +)$ is a commutative group and $(R, \cdot)$ is a commutative monoid such that $x(y+z) = xy + xz$ for all $x, y, z \in R$.

A subring A of R is an ideal iff $rA \subset A$ for all $r \in R$.

Let R and S be commutative rings with identities. $f: R \to S$ is a homomorphism iff it is a homomorphism of both the additive group and the multiplicative monoid.

Definition. A commutative ring K with identity is a field iff every nonzero element of K has a multiplicative inverse.

Definition. Let K be a field and V a commutative group. Let there be given a function $K \times V \to V$ (represented multiplicatively) such that

$$k(x+y) = kx + ky, \quad (k+m)x = kx + mx, \quad k(mx) = (km)x,$$
$$1x = x \quad \text{for all } k, m \in K, \text{ for all } x, y \in V.$$

Then V is a vector space over the field K.

Definition. An algebra V over a field K is a vector space over a field K in which a multiplication is defined $(V \times V \to V)$ such that

$$k(xy) = (kx)y = x(ky), \quad x(yz) = (xy)z,$$
$$x(y+z) = xy + xz, \quad (x+y)z = xz + yz$$

for all $x, y, z \in V$ and for all $k \in K$.

7.1 Let $f: X \to Y$ be given. Then there exists a partition X/R of X, a surjection $\phi: X \twoheadrightarrow X/R$, and an injection $f_1: X/R \rightarrowtail Y$ such that $f_1 \circ \phi = f$. This theorem will be referred to in later exercises as the fundamental mapping theorem.

7.2 A group is an ordered pair (G, w), a set G of elements and a function $w: G \times G \to G$ called an operation. Prove that the set G can be "recaptured" from the set of ordered pairs w; that is, prove that

$$G = \{x \mid x \in \bigcup\bigcup\bigcup\bigcup w \text{ and } ((x, y), z) \in w \text{ for some } y, z\}.$$

7.3 Let $((G_i, w_i))_{i \in I}$ be a nonempty family of groups. Prove that $(\mathop{\mathsf{X}}_{i \in I} G_i, w)$ is a group where w is defined as follows:

$$w: \mathop{\mathsf{X}}_{i \in I} G_i \times \mathop{\mathsf{X}}_{i \in I} G_i \to \mathop{\mathsf{X}}_{i \in I} G_i$$

and

$$w(x, y) = w((x_i)_{i \in I}, (y_i)_{i \in I}) = (w_i(x_i, y_i))_{i \in I}.$$

This group is called the product group.

7.4 Let N be a normal subgroup of a group G. Let $(x, y) \in S$ iff $xy^{-1} \in N$. Prove that S is an equivalence relation on G. Define an operation on the partition G/S as follows: $x/S \cdot y/S = (xy)/S$. Prove that the operation is well-defined, viz., independent of the representative x of the equivalence class x/S. Prove that with respect to the defined operation G/S is a group, and call it the factor group or quotient group G/N; i.e., $G/S = G/N$. Let ϕ be the quotient map $G \twoheadrightarrow G/S$. Prove that ϕ is an epimorphism (by definition a surjective homomorphism). Prove that N is the identity of G/N. Prove that $\phi(e_G) = N$. Prove that $x/S = xN = \phi(x)$.

7.5 Let $f: X \to Y$ be a homomorphism of the group X into the group Y. Then by the fundamental mapping theorem (v.s.) there exist a partition X/T (an equivalence relation T on X with $(x, y) \in T$ iff $f(x) = f(y)$), a surjection $\phi: X \twoheadrightarrow X/T$ (the quotient map), an injection $f_1: X/T \rightarrowtail Y$ such that $f_1 \circ \phi = f$. Let $N = \bar{f}^{-1}(e_Y)$, the kernel of the homomorphism f. Prove that N is a normal subgroup of X and that $(x, y) \in T$ iff $xy^{-1} \in N$. Referring to the previous exercise, see that X/N is a quotient group $(= X/T)$ and ϕ is an epimorphism. Prove that f_1 is a monomorphism (by definition an injective homomorphism). In summary: there exist a quotient group X/N, an epimorphism $\phi: X \twoheadrightarrow X/N$, a monomorphism $f_1: X/N \rightarrowtail Y$ such that $f = f_1 \circ \phi$. Prove that f is a monomorphism iff kernel $f = \{e_X\}$.

7.6 Let A be an ideal of R, a commutative ring with identity. Let $(x, y) \in S$ iff $x - y \in A$. Prove that S is an equivalence relation on R. Define operations $+$, $\cdot$ on the partition R/S as follows:

$$x/S + y/S = (x+y)/S$$
$$x/S \cdot y/S = (xy)/S.$$

Prove that the operations are well-defined on R/S. Prove that R/S is a commutative ring with identity. Denote this ring by R/A and call it the residue class ring or quotient ring. Let ϕ be the quotient map $R \twoheadrightarrow R/S = R/A$. Prove that ϕ is an epimorphism. Prove that $x/S = x + A = \bar{\phi}(x)$.

7.7 Let $f: R \to Q$ be a homomorphism of the ring R into the ring Q. Prove that there exist a quotient ring R/A, an epimorphism $\phi: R \twoheadrightarrow R/A$, a monomorphism $f_1: R/A \rightarrowtail Q$ such that $f = f_1 \circ \phi$.

8 Let $f: X \to Y$. Prove that there exist an equivalence rela-
n S on X, a surjection $\phi: X \twoheadrightarrow X/S$, a bijection g:
$S \rightarrowtail\!\!\twoheadrightarrow f(X)$, and an injection (the identity) $\psi: f(X) \rightarrowtail$
ch that $f = \psi \circ g \circ \phi$.

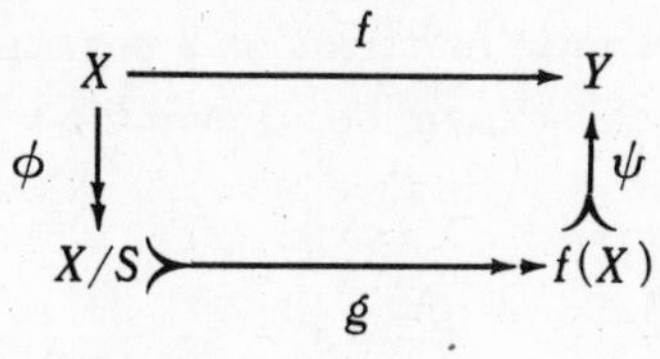

9 Let $p_1: A \times B \twoheadrightarrow A$ such that $p_1(x, y) = x$, $p_2: A \times B$
$\twoheadrightarrow B$ such that $p_2(x, y) = y$. Let $f: X \to A$ and $g: X \to B$.
ove that there exists a unique function $\phi: X \to A \times B$ such that
$\circ \phi = f$ and $p_2 \circ \phi = g$.

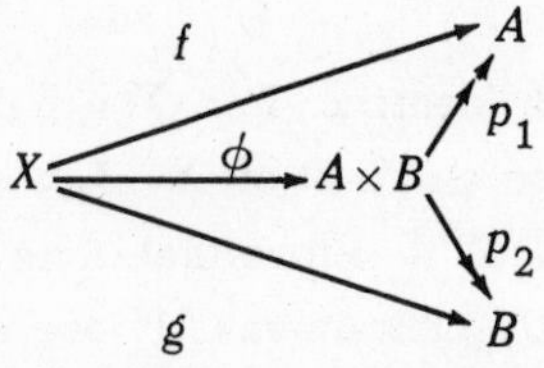

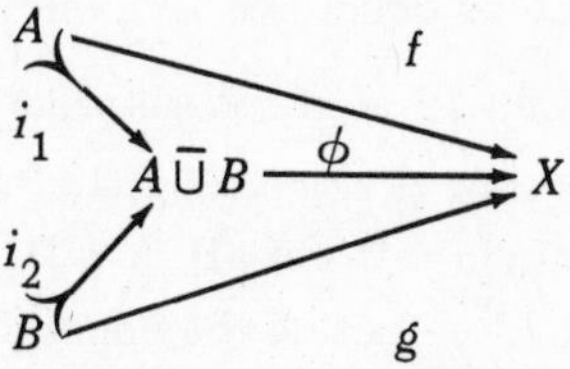

10 Let $A \bar{\cup} B = (A \times \{0\}) \cup (B \times \{1\})$. Let $i_1: A \rightarrowtail A \bar{\cup} B$
ch that $i_1(x) = (x, 0)$. Let $i_2: B \rightarrowtail A \bar{\cup} B$ such that $i_2(x) =$
1). Let $f: A \to X$, $g: B \to X$. Prove that there exists a unique
ction $\phi: A \bar{\cup} B \to X$ such that $\phi \circ i_1 = f$, $\phi \circ i_2 = g$.

11 Let G be a group. Let $X \neq \emptyset$ be a set. For $f, g \in G^X$
fine $fg: X \to G$ such that $(fg)(x) = f(x)g(x)$ for all $x \in X$.
ove that G^X is a group with this defined operation. Prove that if
is a commutative group, then G^X is a commutative group. Prove
at there exists a monomorphism (an injective homomorphism)
$G \rightarrowtail G^X$.

12 Let R be a ring. Let $X \neq \emptyset$ be a set. Prove that there
ist a ring R^X and a monomorphism $\Phi: R \rightarrowtail R^X$ using a simi-
construction to the one in the preceding exercise. Show that it is

possible for R to be a field and R^X not to be a field.

7.13 The set 2 is a ring with the following addition and multipl cation tables: $0+0=0,\ 0+1=1,\ 1+0=1,\ 1+1=0$
$0\cdot 0=0,\ 0\cdot 1=0,\ 1\cdot 0=0,\ 1\cdot 1=1$.
2^X, the set of characteristic functions on a nonempty set X, is then a ring by the preceding exercise. Prove the following results.

$$\chi_{A\cap B} = \chi_A\ \chi_B$$
$$\chi_{A'} = 1-\chi_A$$
$$\chi_{A\cup B} = \chi_A+\chi_B-\chi_A\ \chi_B$$

Prove that the commutative ring with identity $(\mathcal{P}X, +, \cap)$ is isomo phic to the ring $(2^X, +, \cdot)$, The ring $(\mathcal{P}X, +, \cap)$ is called a Bool ring. Note that the operation $(+)$ with the set $\mathcal{P}X$ means symmetr difference as described in Exercise 1.33.

7.14 Let R be a commutative ring with identity. For $X \neq \emptyset$, R^X is a ring by Exercise 7.12. Let D be a subset of X. Let $A = \{f|\ f(x) = 0$ for all $x \in D'$ and $f \in R^X\}$. Prove that A is a ideal of R^X. Let X be nonempty and D' contain exactly one el ment and R be a field. Prove that R^X/A is a ring. Prove that R^X/A is a field.

7.15 Let $X \neq \emptyset$ be a set and K a field. Using the fact that K with addition is a group, prove that K^X is a commutative group. Prove that K^X is a vector space over the field K using the follo ing definition of scalar product: for $k \in K$ and $f \in K^X$ define $kf \in K^X$ such that $(kf)(x) = kf(x)$ for all $x \in X$.

7.16 Let m and n be nonzero natural numbers. Let $I =$ $\{1, 2,\ldots, m\}$ and $J = \{1, 2,\ldots, n\}$ and form the set $I\times J$. Let K be a field. $K^{I\times J}$ is defined to be the set of all m by n matrices over the field K. Use Exercise 7.15 to prove $K^{I\times J}$ is a vector space over the field K. Because $K^{I\times J}$ is a set of functions, any member of $K^{I\times J}$ can be expressed in the family notation (any fur tion is a family and any family is a function). Let $(a_{(i,j)})_{(i,j)\in I\times}$

be an arbitrary member of $K^{I \times J}$. Now to connect with the usual notation for a matrix, simply let the index set be understood and delete a comma and a pair of parentheses: $(a_{ij}) \in K^{I \times J}$. As an exercise write all the defining vector space properties of $K^{I \times J}$ in this family notation.

7.17 Let $J = \{1, 2,\ldots, n\}$ and K be a field. A vector space $K^{J \times J}$ has a product defined as follows: for $f, g \in K^{J \times J}$ define $(fg)(i, j) = \Sigma_{h \in J} f(i, h)g(h, j)$ for all $(i, j) \in J \times J$; $fg \in K^{J \times J}$. Or, in the family notation,

$$(a_{ih})(b_{hj}) = (\sum_{h \in J} a_{ih}\, b_{hj}) .$$

Prove that $K^{J \times J}$, the set of all n square matrices over the field K, is an algebra over K. Prove that the product is noncommutative. Prove that there exists a matrix $(\delta_{ij}) \in K^{J \times J}$ such that

$$(\delta_{ih})(a_{hj}) = (a_{ih})(\delta_{hj}) = (a_{ij}) \quad \text{for all } (a_{ij}) \in K^{J \times J}.$$

7.18 Let E with multiplication be an arbitrary monoid. Let $H = \{h_a | h_a: E \to E,\ a \in E,\ h_a(x) = ax$ for all $x \in E\}$. Prove that H is a submonoid of E^E. Prove that there exists an isomorphism (a bijective homomorphism) $\Phi: E >\!\!\longrightarrow\!\!> H$. Prove that if E is a group, then H is a group (Cayley representation theorem).

7.19 Let $\mathbf{Q}$ be the field of rational numbers and $\mathbf{N}$ the nonnegative integers. Then $\mathbf{Q}^{\mathbf{N}}$ is a ring. Define $s \in \mathbf{Q}^{\mathbf{N}}$ to be a Cauchy sequence iff for $\varepsilon > 0$ there exists an $n \in N$ such that if $i, j \geq n$, then $|s(j) - s(i)| < \varepsilon$ ($\varepsilon \in \mathbf{Q}$ and $i, j \in \mathbf{N}$). Let $S = \{s |\ s \in \mathbf{Q}^{\mathbf{N}}$ and s is Cauchy$\}$. Prove that S is a subring of $\mathbf{Q}^{\mathbf{N}}$. Let $N = \{s |\ s \in S$, and for $\varepsilon > 0$ there exists an n: $|s(i)| < \varepsilon$ for all $i \geq n\}$. Prove that N is an ideal of S. Then S/N is a ring. Prove that S/N is a field (the real numbers). Prove that there exists a monomorphism Φ: $\mathbf{Q} >\!\!\longrightarrow S/N$. This exercise gives the Cauchy sequence construction of the real numbers from the rational numbers.

7.20 Define the nth permutation group $\mathfrak{S}_n$ to be the set of all bijections of the set n with composition as the operation. Let $s \in \mathfrak{S}_n$ and let

$$D = \prod_{0 \leq i < j < n} (x_j - x_i) .$$

$$s(kD) = \prod_{0 \leq i < j < n} (x_{s(j)} - x_{s(i)})$$

by definition. Define the sign of the permutation s as $\varepsilon(s) = s(D)/D$. s is odd if $\varepsilon(s) = -1$ and even if $\varepsilon(s) = 1$. Prove that ε is a homomorphism from $\mathfrak{S}_n$ to the multiplicative group $\{1, -1\}$. The kernel of the homomorphism ε is called the alternating subgroup $\mathfrak{A}_n$ of $\mathfrak{S}_n$. Construct $\mathfrak{S}_0$, $\mathfrak{A}_0$, $\mathfrak{S}_1$, $\mathfrak{A}_1$, $\mathfrak{S}_2$, $\mathfrak{A}_2$, $\mathfrak{S}_3$, $\mathfrak{A}_3$.

CHAPTER 8

THE NATURAL NUMBERS

8.0 Definition. The successor of the set x is the set $x^+ = x \cup \{x\}$. (NST p44)

Definition. A successor set is a set A such that $0 \in A$, and if $x \in A$, then $x^+ \in A$. (NST p44)

Axiom of Infinity. There exists a successor set. (NST p44)

Definition of ω, the Set of Natural Numbers. Let A be a successor set. Then $\omega = \bigcap \{S \mid S \in \mathcal{P}A$ and S is a successor set$\}$. (NST p44)

Five Theorems on ω (the Peano Axioms).

I) $0 \in \omega$.

II) If $n \in \omega$, then $n^+ \in \omega$.

III) If $S \subset \omega$ and if $0 \in S$ and if $n^+ \in S$ whenever $n \in S$, then $S = \omega$.

IV) $n^+ \neq 0$ for all $n \in \omega$.

V) If $m, n \in \omega$ and $m^+ = n^+$, then $m = n$. (NST p46)

Two Lemmas on ω. i) For all $n \in \omega$ it is never the case that $x \in n$ and $n \subset x$. ii) If $x \in n$, then $x \subset n$ for all $n \in \omega$. (NST p47)

The Recursion Theorem for ω. If $a \in X$ and $f\colon X \to X$, then there exists a $u\colon \omega \to X$ such that $u(0) = a$ and $u(n^+) = f(u(n))$ for all $n \in \omega$. (NST p48)

Definitions. A finite set E is a set equivalent to some member of

ω. A set not finite is an infinite set. The number of element in a finite set is the unique member of ω to which the set is equivalent. (NST p53)

A countable set is a set equivalent to ω or a member of ω. (NST p91)

8.1 On page 42 of NST it is stated that all unordered pairs do not constitute a set. Prove this assertion.

8.2 Prove ω is a transitive set: if $x \in \omega$ then $x \subset \omega$.

8.3 Prove this property of ω: if E is a nonempty subset of ω then there exists a $k \in E$ such that $k \in m$ for all $m \in E$, $m \neq k$.

8.4 Let $m, n \in \omega$. Prove $m \in n$ iff $m^+ \in n^+$.

8.5 Prove that $n \notin n$ for all $n \in \omega$, the set of natural numbers.

8.6 If $n \in \omega$ and $n \neq 0$, then $0 \in n$.

8.7 The finite union of finite sets is finite.

8.8 No set with two elements can be a subset of a set with one element.

8.9 Let $(A_i)_{i \in \omega}$ be a family such that $A_i \subsetneqq A_{i^+}$ for all $i \in \omega$. Prove that $A_0 \subsetneqq A_n$ for all $n \in \omega$, $n \neq 0$.

8.10 On page 47 of NST a proof of Peano Axiom V is given using two lemmas (the two lemmas are cited in 8.0). Give a proof of Peano Axiom V using only the second lemma: prove $n^+ = m^+$ implies $n = m$.

8.11 Let $(A_i)_{i \in \omega}$ be a family such that $A_i \subset A_{i^+}$ for all $i \in \omega$. Furthermore, let $\bigcup_{i \in \omega} A_i \subset A_0$. Prove that $A_i = A_j$ for all i, $j \in \omega$.

8.12 Let $(X_i)_{i \in \omega}$ be a sequence of sets. Define

$$\liminf (X_i)_{i \in \omega} = \bigcup_{j \in \omega} \bigcap_{i \in \omega - j^+} X_i = \bigcup_{j \in \omega} \bigcap_{\substack{i \in \omega \\ i > j}} X_i$$

$$\limsup (X_i)_{i \in \omega} = \bigcap_{j \in \omega} \bigcup_{\substack{i \in \omega \\ i > j}} X_i \quad .$$

Prove that $\lim\inf(X_i)_{i\in\omega} \subset \lim\sup(X_i)_{i\in\omega}$.

8.13 If $\lim\inf(X_i)_{i\in\omega} = \lim\sup(X_i)_{i\in\omega}$, then by definition

$$\lim(X_i)_{i\in\omega} = \lim\inf(X_i)_{i\in\omega} = \lim\sup(X_i)_{i\in\omega}.$$

Find the limits in the following examples:

$X_i = [0, i] \subset \mathbf{R}$, the set of real numbers,
$X_i = [0, 1/i]$,
$X_i = [0, 1]$ for i even, $[0, -1]$ for i odd.

8.14 A sequence is defined to be increasing (with respect to $\subset$) provided $X_i \subset X_{i^+}$ and decreasing provided $X_{i^+} \subset X_i$ for all $i \in \omega$. Prove that increasing and decreasing sequences always have limits and that $\lim(X_i)_{i\in\omega} = \bigcup_{i\in\omega} X_i$ for the increasing sequence and $\lim(X_i)_{i\in\omega} = \bigcap_{i\in\omega} X_i$ for the decreasing sequence.

8.15 The recursion theorem is stated in 8.0. In each of the following examples state what are f, a, u, X.

a) s_m, addition of natural numbers,
b) p_m, multiplication of natural numbers,
c) e_m, exponentiation of natural numbers,
d) $u(n) = d^n g/dx^n$, differentiation of functions,
e) $u(n) = g^n$, composition of functions.

8.16 For any $x \in \omega$, s_x is the function from ω to ω defined recursively as follows: $s_x(0) = x$, $s_x(n^+) = [s_x(n)]^+$. Utilizing the functions s_x, define an operation on ω as follows:

$$s = \{((x, y), z) \mid ((x, y), z) \in (\omega \times \omega) \times \omega \text{ and } z = s_x(y)\}.$$

Prove that s is a set, a function, and an operation on ω. Prove that ω with the operation s is a commutative monoid. Prove that ω is a semigroup.

8.17 For any $x \in \omega$, p_x is the function from ω to ω defined recursively as follows: $p_x(0) = 0$, $p_x(n^+) = p_x(n) + x = s(p_x(n), x)$. Utilizing the functions p_x define an operation on ω as follows:

$$p = \{((x, y), z) \mid ((x, y), z) \in (\omega \times \omega) \times \omega \text{ and } z = p_x(y)\}.$$

Prove that ω with the operation p is a commutative monoid. Also prove these theorems: For all $x, y, z \in \omega$

a) $x(y+z) = xy + xz$,

b) $x + 1 = x^+$,

c) $x + y = 0$ implies $x = 0$ and $y = 0$,

d) $xy = 0$ implies $x = 0$ or $y = 0$,

e) $x + y = 1$ implies $x = 1$ or $y = 1$,

f) $xy = 1$ implies $x = 1$ and $y = 1$.

8.18 Construction of the Integers. Let $\mathbf{N}$ be the set of natural numbers with the operations of addition and multiplication. Prove that R defined as follows is an equivalence relation on $\mathbf{N} \times \mathbf{N}$: $((x, y), (u, v)) \in R$ iff $x + v = y + u$. Upon the partition $(\mathbf{N} \times \mathbf{N})/R$ define two operations:

$$(x, y)/R + (u, v)/R = (x + u, y + v)/R$$
$$(x, y)/R \cdot (u, v)/R = (xu + yv, xv + yu)/R.$$

Prove that these operations are well-defined (independent of the representatives chosen), and show furthermore that they are commutative and associative and that $(\cdot)$ is distributive with respect to $(+)$. Define $\Phi: \mathbf{N} \rightarrowtail (\mathbf{N} \times \mathbf{N})/R$ so that $\Phi(x) = (x, 0)/R$. Show that Φ is a monomorphism for both operations. This monomorphism Φ identifies certain integers with the natural numbers. The notation for the natural number x and the integer $\Phi(x)$ are used interchangeably.

For simplicity, define $\mathbf{Z} = (\mathbf{N} \times \mathbf{N})/R$ with the two operations $(+)$ and $(\cdot)$ to be the integers. Show that every member of $\mathbf{Z}$ has a negative: for all $\alpha \in (\mathbf{N} \times \mathbf{N})/R$ there exists a $\beta \in (\mathbf{N} \times \mathbf{N})/R$ such that $\alpha + \beta = \Phi(0)$. Prove that $\mathbf{Z}$ is a commutative ring with an identity. Prove furthermore that nonzero multiplicative cancellation is possible: $\alpha\beta = \alpha\gamma$ and $\alpha \neq 0$ implies $\beta = \gamma$.

8.19 Construction of the Rational Numbers. Let $\mathbf{Z}$ be the set of integers. Let $\mathbf{Z}^* = \mathbf{Z} - \{0\}$. Prove that S defined as follows is an equivalence relation on $\mathbf{Z} \times \mathbf{Z}^*$: $((x, y), (u, v)) \in S$ iff $xv = yu$. On $(\mathbf{Z} \times \mathbf{Z}^*)/S$ define

$$(x, y)/S + (u, v)/S = (xv + yu, yv)/S$$
$$(x, y)/S \cdot (u, v)/S = (xu, yv)/S.$$

Prove that these operations are well defined, that they are both commutative and associative, and that $(\cdot)$ is distributive with respect to $(+)$. Define $\Omega\colon \mathbf{Z} \rightarrowtail (\mathbf{Z} \times \mathbf{Z}^*)/S$ such that $\Omega(x) = (x, 1)/S$. Prove that Ω is a monomorphism. Thus the integers are isomorphic with a subset of $(\mathbf{Z} \times \mathbf{Z}^*)/S$. Define $\mathbf{Q} = (\mathbf{Z} \times \mathbf{Z}^*)/S$ to be the rational numbers. Prove that $\mathbf{Q}$ is a commutative ring with identity. Prove that if $\alpha \in \mathbf{Q}$ and $\alpha \neq 0$, then there exists $\beta \in \mathbf{Q}$ such that $\alpha\beta = \Omega(1)$ or 1. Hence $\mathbf{Q}$ is a field.

8.20 X is defined to be Dedekind infinite iff there exists an injection $f\colon X \rightarrowtail X$ such that $f(X) \subsetneq X$. X is defined to be infinite iff X is not equivalent to any member of ω. Prove that X is infinite iff X is Dedekind infinite.

8.21 Prove that X is countable iff X is equivalent to some subset of ω. Prove that a subset of a countable set is countable.

8.22 Let $f\colon X \twoheadrightarrow Y$ with X countable. Prove that Y is countable.

8.23 Prove that ω is equivalent to $\omega \times \omega$. Prove that the countable union of countable sets is countable.

8.24 No natural number is a member of itself. To extend this regularity to sets in general, the following axiom is often adjoined to the ones previously taken: If $X \neq \emptyset$, then there exists a set x such that $x \in X$ and $x \cap X = \emptyset$. Prove that the axiom of regularity implies $x \notin x$ for all sets x.

8.25 Prove (using the axiom of regularity) that $x \notin y$ or $y \notin x$, for all x, y.

8.26 Prove (using the axiom of regularity) that given the family $(a_i)_{i \in \omega}$, $a_{i+1} \notin a_i$ for some $i \in \omega$.

8.27 Give an example of a family $(a_i)_{i \in \omega}$ such that $a_i \in a_{i+1}$ for all $i \in \omega$.

8.28 Prove that if $X \subset X \times X$, then $X = \emptyset$. Hint: axiom of regularity.

CHAPTER 9

ORDER

9.0 $(X, \leq)$ is an ordered set means X is a set and $\leq$ is an order on X. If the existence of the order is to be understood, then it is simply said that X is an ordered set. (NST p55)

Definition. X is a totally ordered set iff $x, y \in X$ implies $x \leq y$ or $y \leq x$. (NST p54)

Definitions. Let X be an ordered set. Let a be an element of X.

a is a minimal element of X iff there is no $x \in X$ such that $x < a$,

a is a maximal element of X iff there is no $x \in X$ such that $a < x$.

a is a minimum element of X or least element of x iff $a \leq x$ for all $x \in X$.

a is a maximum element of X or greatest element of x iff $x \leq a$ for all $x \in X$. (NST p56)

Definitions. Let X be an ordered set. Let S be a subset of X. Let $a \in X$.

a is an upper bound for S iff $x \leq a$ for all $x \in S$.

a is a lower bound for S iff $a \leq x$ for all $x \in S$.

inf S or glb S is the maximum of the set of lower bounds of S.

sup S or lub S is the minimum of the set of upper bounds of S. (NST p57)

Definition. Let X be an ordered set. X is a well ordered set iff every nonempty subset of X has a minimum element. (NST p66)

9.1 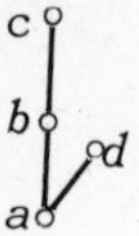

This is a diagram for the ordered set (X, S) where $X = \{a, b, c, d\}$ and the order $S = \{(a, a), (a, b), (a, c), (a, d), (b, b), (b, c), (c, c), (d, d)\} = \{(a, b), (a, c), (a, d), (b, c)\} \cup I_X$.

What is the set and order for the following two diagrams?

a) 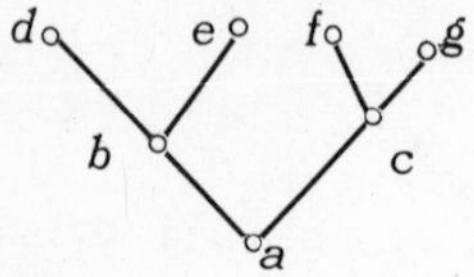

b) 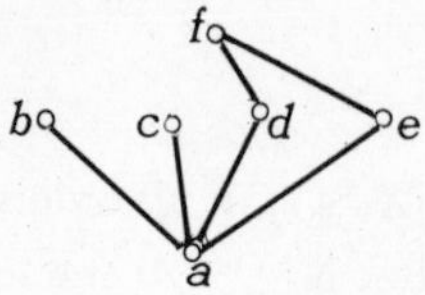

9.2 Draw diagrams for the following ordered sets (X, S).

a) $X = \{a, b, c, d, e\}$, $S = \{(a, d), (a, c), (a, b), (a, e), (b, e), (c, e), (d, e)\} \cup I_X$,

b) $X = \{a, b, c, d, e, f, g\}$, $S = \{(a, g), (b, g), (c, g), (g, e), (g, f), (a, e), (a, f), (b, e), (b, f), (c, e), (c, f)\} \cup I_X$,

c) $X = \{a, b, c, d\}$, $S = \{(c, d)\} \cup I_X$,

d) $X = \mathcal{P}\{a, b, c\}$, $S = (\subset)$.

For each example discuss which elements are maximal, minimal, maximum, minimum.

9.3 Let $X = \{a, b, c, d, e\}$ and let $S = \{(a, c), (b, c), (d, e)\}$. Prove that S is a strict order on X, is not total, and has three minimal and two maximal elements. Note that a strict order is total iff $x, y \in X$ and $x \neq y$ implies $x\, S\, y$ or $y\, S\, x$.

9.4 Prove that if an ordered set X has two distinct minimal elements, then it has no minimum element.

9.5 Let X be an ordered set. Let A be a finite totally ordered subset of X and let $a = \sup A$. Prove that $a = \text{maximum } A$. Give an example where A is not totally ordered and the conclusion is false.

9.6 Let Q be the set of all orders on a given set X. $(Q, \subset)$ is itself an ordered set. Prove that T is a maximal element of

$(Q, \subset)$ iff T is total. Draw a diagram for $(Q, \subset)$ in the case where $X = 3$.

9.7 Let S be an antisymmetric relation on X. By example, prove it may be the case that there exists no order T such that $S \subset T$. In other words, not every antisymmetric relation may be extended to an order.

9.8 Let X be an ordered set such that every nonempty subset A of X with an upper bound in X has a least upper bound in X. Prove that every nonempty subset B of X with a lower bound in X has a greatest lower bound in X.

9.9 Let X and Y be ordered sets and let $f\colon X \twoheadrightarrow Y$ be a surjection. Let $x \leq y$ iff $f(x) \leq f(y)$ for all $x, y \in X$. Prove that f is an injection.

9.10 Let X be an ordered set. For $a \in X$ let $s(a) = \{x \mid x \in X \text{ and } x < a\}$, $\bar{s}(a) = \{x \mid x \in X \text{ and } x \leq a\}$. Prove that

$$\bigcup_{a \in X} s(a) \subset X; \qquad \bigcup_{a \in X} \bar{s}(a) = X;$$

if $X \neq \emptyset$, then $\bigcap_{a \in X} s(a) = \emptyset$;

$$\bigcap_{a \in X} \bar{s}(a) = \{\text{minimum } X\} \text{ if minimum } X \text{ exists;}$$

$$= \emptyset \text{ otherwise.}$$

9.11 Let $S(X) = \{s(a) \mid a \in X\}$ where X is given as an ordered set. On $S(X)$ define an order: $s(a) \leq s(b)$ iff $a \leq b$. Prove that $S(X)$ is an ordered set and is totally ordered iff X is totally ordered.

9.12 Let $(S_i)_{i \in I}$ be a nonempty family of equivalence relations on X totally ordered by inclusion. Prove that $\bigcup_{i \in I} S_i$ is an equivalence relation on X.

9.13 Let $(S_i)_{i \in I}$ be a nonempty family of orders on X totally ordered by inclusion. Prove that $\bigcup_{i \in I} S_i$ is an order on X.

CHAPTER 10

THE AXIOM OF CHOICE AND ZORN'S LEMMA

10.0 Axiom of Choice. Let $(X_i)_{i \in I}$ be given such that $I \neq \emptyset$ and $X_i \neq \emptyset$ for all $i \in I$. Then $\times_{i \in I} X_i \neq \emptyset$. (NST p59)

Definition. f is a choice function for X iff $f\colon \mathcal{P}X - \{\emptyset\} \to X$ such that $f(A) \in A$. (NST p60)

Axiom of Choice (Alternate Formulation). For every set X there exists a choice function. (NST p60)

Definition. A chain in X is a totally ordered subset of X. (NST p62)

Zorn's Lemma. If X is a nonempty ordered set such that every chain in X has an upper bound in X, then X contains a maximal element. (NST p62)

Definition. A family of vectors $(x_i)_{i \in I}$ in a vector space V over a field K generates V iff for every $x \in V$ there is a finite subset J of I such that $x = \Sigma_{i \in J}\, k_i x_i$, $k_i \in K$.

Definition. A family of vectors $(x_i)_{i \in I}$ in a vector space V over a field K is linearly independent iff whenever $J \subset I$ and J is finite and $\Sigma_{i \in J}\, k_i x_i = 0$, $k_i \in K$, then $k_i = 0$ for all $i \in J$.

Definition. A family of vectors $(x_i)_{i \in I}$ in a vector space V over a field K is a basis iff $(x_i)_{i \in I}$ is linearly independent and generates V.

10.1 Let $n \in \omega$, $n \neq 0$ and let $(X_i)_{i \in n}$ be a family of nonempty sets. Prove that $\times_{i \in n} X_i \neq 0$ without using the axiom of choice.

10.2 Let $\mathcal{X}$ be a collection of sets and let $\mathcal{Y} = \{B \mid B \subset A$ for some $A \in \mathcal{X}\}$. Prove that $\mathcal{Y}$ is a set and furthermore that M is a maximal element of $\mathcal{Y}$ iff M is a maximal element of $\mathcal{X}$.

10.3 Prove that the following proposition implies Zorn's lemma and is implied by it. Let $\mathcal{X} \neq \emptyset$ be a set of sets ordered by inclusion. For every nonempty chain $\mathcal{C}$ in $\mathcal{X}$ let $\bigcup \mathcal{C} \in \mathcal{X}$. Then $\mathcal{X}$ has a maximal element.

10.4 Let R be a commutative ring with an identity. Prove that every proper ideal $(\neq R)$ of R is included in a maximal proper ideal of R.

10.5 If V is a vector space over the field K, then it has a basis.

10.6 If T is an order on the set X, then there exists an order $\overline{T}$ on X such that $T \subset \overline{T}$ and $\overline{T}$ is total.

10.7 Prove that there exists an $f\colon \mathbf{R} \to \mathbf{R}$ such that $f(x+y) = f(x) + f(y)$. Prove that not every such f is of the form $f(x) = kx$ for some $k \in \mathbf{R}$.

10.8 Prove that the following proposition, called the Kuratowski lemma, is equivalent to Zorn's lemma. Each chain in an ordered set $(X, \leq)$ is included in a maximal chain.

10.9 Prove that the following proposition, called the Zermelo postulate, is equivalent to the Axiom of Choice. Given $\mathcal{X}$, a disjoint set of nonempty sets, then there is a set F such that $X \cap F$ is a singleton for each $X \in \mathcal{X}$.

CHAPTER 11

WELL ORDERING

11.0 Definition. An ordered set X is a well ordered set iff every nonempty subset of X contains a minimum element. (NST p66)

Definition. In an ordered set X the open initial segment determined by $a \in X$ is the set $s(a) = \{x | x \in X \text{ and } x < a\}$. (NST p56)

Theorems (Principle of Transfinite Induction for Well Ordered Sets). If X is a well ordered set and $S \subset X$ such that $s(a) \subset S$ implies $a \in S$, then $S = X$. (NST p66)

(The Well Ordering Theorem.) If X is a set, then there is an order R on X so that (X, R) is a well ordered set. (NST p68)

11.1 Let (X, T) be an ordered set. Let A be a subset of X. Then prove that a is the minimum element of A iff image $(T \cap (\{a\} \times A)) = A$.

11.2 Let (X, T) be a well ordered set. Prove that $f = \{(A, a) | (A, a) \in (\mathcal{P} X - 1) \times X \text{ and image } (T \cap (\{a\} \times A)) = A\}$ is a set. What is the significance of the set f ?

11.3 Prove that every subset of a well ordered set is well ordered.

11.4 Let X be a set and $\mathfrak{X} = \{(A, R) | A \subset X \text{ and } R \text{ is an order on } A\}$. Prove that the relations defined as follows are all orders on $\mathfrak{X}$:

$(A, R) <_1 (B, S)$ iff $A \subset B$ and $R \subset S$,
$(A, R) <_2 (B, S)$ iff $A \subset B$ and $R = S \cap (A \times A)$,
$(A, R) <_3 (B, S)$ iff $[A = B$ or
$A = \{x \mid x \in B$ and $(x, b) \in S - I_B\}$ for some $b \in B]$
and $R \subset S$,
$(A, R) <_4 (B, S)$ iff $[A = B$ or
$A = \{x \mid x \in B$ and $(x, b) \in S - I_B\}$ for some $b \in B]$
and $R = S \cap (A \times A)$.

hich orders are stronger? $(<_i)$ is stronger than $(<_j)$ iff (A, R) $_i$ (B, S) implies $(A, R) <_j (B, S)$ for all $(A, R), (B, S) \in \mathfrak{X}$. his is to say, $(<_i) \subset (<_j)$.

1.5 Let A be an initial segment of a well ordered set $(X, \leq)$. rove that an initial segment of A (an ordered set by the restriction f the order on X) is an initial segment of X. Prove that an initial egment of X is an initial segment of A or includes A.

1.6 The Well Ordering Theorem (NST p69). Let X be a set. rove that $\mathfrak{W} = \{(A, R) \mid A \subset X$ and R well orders $A\}$ is a nonmpty set. Define $(A, R) < (B, S)$ iff $[A = \{x \mid x \in B$ and (x, b) $S - I_B\}$ for some $b \in B]$ and $R = S \cap (A \times A)$ or, in less foral terms, A and B are the same ordered set, or A is an initial egment of B. Prove that $(<)$, in NST called continuation, is an rder on $\mathfrak{W}$. Let $\mathcal{C}$ be a chain in $\mathfrak{W}$. Show that ($\bigcup$ preimage $\mathcal{C}$, image $\mathcal{C}$) $\in \mathfrak{W}$ and that ($\bigcup$ preimage $\mathcal{C}$, $\bigcup$ image $\mathcal{C}$) is an upper bound r $\mathcal{C}$. Use Zorn's lemma to show that $\mathfrak{W}$ has a maximal element $C, T)$. Prove that $C = X$ and conclude T is a well ordering of X.

1.7 Prove that there exists an ordered set (X, S) such that if T rders X and $S \subset T$ then (X, T) is not well ordered.

1.8 A subset A of an ordered set X is cofinal in X in case r each element x of X there exists an element a of A such at $x \leq a$. Prove that every totally ordered set has a cofinal well rdered subset. (NST p68)

11.9 The following form of the principle of transfinite induction is often found in the literature. If X is a well ordered set and $S \subset X$ such that $s(a) \subset S$ implies $a \in S$ and minimum $X \in S$, then $S = X$. Show that the condition minimum $X \in S$ is superfluous.

CHAPTER 12

TRANSFINITE RECURSION AND SIMILARITY

12.0 Transfinite Recursion Theorem. Let W be a well ordered set. Let $f: \mathfrak{W} \to X$ where $\mathfrak{W} = \{\phi \mid \phi: s(a) \to X$ for some $a \in W\}$. Then there exists $U: W \to X$ such that $U(a) = f(U \mid s(a))$. (NST p70)

Definition. Let (X, R) and (Y, S) be ordered sets. $f: X \rightarrowtail\!\!\twoheadrightarrow Y$ is a similarity means $(x_1, x_2) \in R$ iff $(f(x_1), f(x_2)) \in S$. (NST p 71)

$f: X \to Y$ is an order-preserving function means $(x_1, x_2) \in R$ implies $(f(x_1), f(x_2)) \in S$.

Theorem. If f is a similarity of X with a subset of itself and X is well ordered, then $x \leq f(x)$ for all $x \in X$. (NST p72)

Theorem. There is at most one similarity from a well ordered set X onto a well ordered set Y. (NST p72)

Theorem. A well ordered set is never similar to one of its initial segments. (NST p73)

Theorem. If X and Y are well ordered sets, then one of these statements is true:

a) X is similar to Y,

b) X is similar to an initial segment of Y,

c) Y is similar to an initial segment of X. (NST p73)

Definition. A nonempty ordered set $(L, \leq)$ is a lattice iff every pair of elements of L has a least upper bound and a greatest lower bound in L. A lattice $(L, \leq)$ is complete iff every every subset of L has a least upper bound and a greatest lower bound in L.

12.1 ω is a well ordered set. Let $N \in \omega - 1$; $a_0, a_1, \dots a_{N-1} \in$ R; $F\colon \mathrm{R}^N \to \mathrm{R}$ be given. Using transfinite recursion prove there exists a function $u\colon \omega \to \mathrm{R}$ such that $u(0) = a_0$, $u(1) = a_1, \dots,$ $u(N-1) = a_{N-1}$ and $u(n) = F(u(n-N), u(n-N+1), \dots,$ $u(n-2), u(n-1))$ for $n \geq N$.

12.2 As an example of the theorem established in Exercise 12.1, consider this exercise in recursive definition. In the quest for a series solution of a differential equation such as $y'' + A(x)y' + B(x)y = 0$ with $y(0) = 0$, $y'(0) = 1$ one substitutes $y = \Sigma_{i \in \omega}\, a_i x^i$ into the differential equation and compares coefficients. Determine the value of $(a_i)_{i \in \omega}$ by a recursion formula which will be F in the preceding theorem $(N = 2)$. Conclude that the sequence $(a_i)_{i \in \omega}$ is defined and thus the power series $\Sigma_{i \in \omega}\, a_i x^i$.

12.3 Show that $f\colon \omega \to \omega - \{0\}$ such that $f(n) = n^+$ is a similarity.

12.4 Let $f\colon X \rightarrowtail\!\!\!\twoheadrightarrow Y$ be a similarity from the ordered set $(X, \leq)$ to the ordered set $(Y, \leq)$. Prove that if $(X, \leq)$ is totally ordered, then $(Y, \leq)$ is totally ordered. Prove that if $(X, \leq)$ is well ordered, then $(Y, \leq)$ is well ordered.

12.5 Let $(X, \leq)$, $(Y, \leq)$ be ordered sets. Then a bijection $f\colon X \rightarrowtail\!\!\!\twoheadrightarrow Y$ is a similarity iff $x_1 < x_2$ when and only when $f(x_1) < f(x_2)$ for all $x_1, x_2 \in X$.

12.6 Let X and Y be ordered sets. Prove that if the bijection $f\colon X \rightarrowtail\!\!\!\twoheadrightarrow Y$ is order preserving and X is totally ordered, then f is a similarity.

12.7 Prove that the set of all similarities of an ordered set X form a subgroup of the symmetric group on X.

12.8 Let X and Y be ordered sets and $f\colon X \rightarrowtail\!\!\!\twoheadrightarrow Y$ be a similarity. Then prove that $f(\sup A) = \sup(f(A))$ for all $A \subset X$ for which $\sup A$ exists. (NST p73)

12.9 Let $f\colon \omega \to \omega$ be given satisfying the condition $f(2^n) = n^2$. For what values of $n \in \omega$ can f possibly be a similarity of ω onto a subset of ω?

12.10 What are the similarities of ω?

12.11 Prove that the only similarities of **Z** are the translations, i.e., of the form $f(x) = x + n$, $n \in \mathbf{Z}$.

12.12 Show that the similarity subgroup of **Z** is equivalent to **Z** under the natural bijection Φ defined in Exercise 7.18. Order the similarity subgroup so that Φ becomes a similarity.

12.13 Prove that f defined by $f(x) = ax + b$ is a similarity of **R** if $a > 0$. Prove that these are not the only similarities of **R**.

12.14 If E is the set of all equivalence relations on X, and F is the set of all partitions of X, and $\Phi\colon E \rightarrowtail\!\!\twoheadrightarrow F$ is the natural bijection, prove that Φ is a similarity for the ordered sets $(E, \subset)$ and $(F,$ is finer then).

12.15 Prove that E, the set of all equivalence relations on a non-empty set X, is a complete lattice. Prove that the image of a complete lattice under a similarity is also a complete lattice. Conclude that F, the set of all partitions of X, is a complete lattice.

12.16 $f; X \rightarrowtail\!\!\twoheadrightarrow Y$ is an antisimilarity of the ordered sets $(X, R), (Y, S)$ means $x_1 \leq x_2$ iff $f(x_2) \leq f(x_1)$ for all $x_1, x_2 \in X$. Let $f\colon X \rightarrowtail\!\!\twoheadrightarrow Y$ be an antisimilarity of the ordered sets (X, R), (Y, S). Then prove that f is a similarity for the ordered sets $(X, R), (Y, S^{-1})$.

12.17 Let $f\colon X \rightarrowtail\!\!\twoheadrightarrow Y$ be an antisimilarity of the ordered sets $(X, R), (Y, S)$ and let (X, R) be well ordered. Then prove that (Y, S^{-1}) is well ordered.

12.18 $f\colon X \rightarrowtail\!\!\twoheadrightarrow Y$ is a similarity for the ordered sets (X, R), (Y, S) iff $f\colon X \rightarrowtail\!\!\twoheadrightarrow Y$ is a similarity for the ordered sets $(X, R^{-1}), (Y, S^{-1})$.

12.19 Let $f: X \rightarrowtail\!\!\!\twoheadrightarrow Y$ be a similarity for the ordered sets (X, R), (Y, S). If at least one of the sets (X, R), (X, R^{-1}), (Y, S), (Y, S^{-1}) is well ordered, then f is the only similarity from X to Y.

12.20 Define (X, S) to be doubly well ordered iff every nonempty subset of X has both a minimum element and a maximum element. Prove that (X, S) is doubly well ordered iff (X, S) and (X, S^{-1}) are well ordered. Prove that no infinite subset of ω can be doubly well ordered, and hence prove that no infinite set can be doubly well ordered.

12.21 Are there antisimilarities of ω? of $\mathbf{Z}$? of the real interval $(0, +\infty)$?

12.22 Give a counterexample to this proposition (an analogy to a theorem on equivalence given on p88 of NST). If X and Y are ordered sets, and X is similar to a subset of Y, and Y is similar to a subset of X, then X is similar to Y.

CHAPTER 13

ORDINALS

13.0 The Axiom of Substitution. If $S(a, b)$ is a sentence such that each a in a set A the set $\{b|\ S(a, b)\}$ can be formed, then there exists a function F with domain A such that $F(a) = \{b|\ S(a, b)\}$ for each a in A. (NST p75)

Definition. α is an ordinal number iff α is a well ordered set such that $s(\xi) = \xi$ for all $\xi \in \alpha$. (NST p75)

Theorem. If α is an ordinal, then α^+ is an ordinal. (NST p75)

Theorem. If α is an ordinal and $\beta \in \alpha$, then β is an ordinal. (NST p78)

Theorem. If α and β are similar ordinals, then $\alpha = \beta$. (NST p78)

Theorem. Any set of ordinals is totally ordered, and for any two distinct ordinals α and β the following are equivalent: $\alpha \in \beta$, $\alpha \subset \beta$, β is a continuation of α. (NST p79)

Theorem. Any set of ordinals is well ordered. (NST p79)

Definition. An infinite ordinal which is the successor of no ordinal is called a limit ordinal. (NST p79)

Theorem. For any set of ordinals there exists an ordinal which is a supremum for the set. (NST p80)

Counting Theorem. Every well ordered set is similar to a unique ordinal. (NST p80)

Definition. The ordinal sum of the disjoint well ordered sets (A, R)

and (B, S) is the well ordered set $(A \cup B, R \cup (A \times A) \cup S)$. (NST p82)

Definition. The ordinal product of the well ordered sets (A, R) and (B, S) is the well ordered set $(A \times B, T)$ where $((a_1, b_1), (a_2, b_2)) \in T$ iff $(b_1 = b_2$ and $(a_1, a_2) \in R)$ or $(b_1, b_2) \in S - I_B$. (NST p83) Cf. also Exercise 3.31.

Definition. The sum $\alpha + \beta$ of the ordinals α and β is the unique ordinal similar to the ordinal sum of the well ordered sets $\alpha \times \{0\}$ and $\beta \times \{1\}$. (NST p82)

Definition. The product $\alpha\beta$ of the ordinals α and β is the unique ordinal similar to the ordinal product of the well ordered sets α and β. (NST p83)

13.1 ω is the minimum successor set in that if A is any successor set, then $\omega \subset A$. Is there a maximum or maximal successor set in a given nonempty set of successor sets? Is there a maximal or maximum successor set?

13.2 Assume that $\emptyset$ is a set and the axiom of substitution. Prove the axiom of specification.

13.3 Prove that the axiom of substitution together with the power axiom and the existence of $\emptyset$ imply the axiom of pairing.

13.4 α is an ordinal iff α is a set well ordered by ϵ and

$$x \in \alpha \quad \text{implies} \quad x \subset \alpha.$$

13.5 If α is a set totally ordered by ϵ and if $x \in \alpha$ implies $x \subset \alpha$ and the axiom of regularity is assumed, then α is an ordinal. Cf. Exercise 8.20 for a statement of the axiom of regularity.

13.6 If α is an ordinal there is no ordinal β so that $\alpha < \beta < \alpha^+$.

13.7 If α is an ordinal, then $\alpha \notin \alpha$.

13.8 If α is an ordinal, then there is no set x such that $x \in \alpha$ and $\alpha \subset x$.

13.9 ω is an ordinal.

13.10 Each natural number is an ordinal.

13.11 Every ordinal is an initial segment of some other ordinal.

13.12 If A is a nonempty set of ordinals, then $\min A = \bigcap A$.

13.13 Let α be a nonzero ordinal. Then α is a limit ordinal iff $\alpha = \bigcup \alpha$.

13.14 $\bigcup \alpha^+ = \alpha$.

13.15 If α and β are ordinals and $\beta < \alpha$, then $\beta \leq \bigcup \alpha$.

13.16 If α is an ordinal number and α is a finite set then α is a natural number.

13.17 If X is a finite totally ordered set, then X is similar to some natural number.

13.18 Prove, using Zorn's lemma and the axiom of substitution, that every well ordered set is similar to some ordinal.

13.19 $\alpha + 0 = \alpha$ and $0 + \alpha = \alpha$ for all ordinals α.

13.20 $\alpha + 1 = \alpha^+$ for all ordinals α.

13.21 Give an example of an ordinal α such that $1 + \alpha \neq \alpha^+$.

13.22 Give an example of an ordinal β such that $1 + \beta = \beta^+$.

13.23 Prove the associative law for the addition of ordinals.

13.24 Let α and β be ordinals. $\alpha < \beta$ iff there exists an ordinal $\gamma \neq 0$ such that $\alpha + \gamma = \beta$.

13.25 If $\gamma > 0$, then $\alpha + \gamma > \alpha$.

13.26 If $\gamma + \alpha = \gamma + \beta$, then $\alpha = \beta$.

13.27 Prove that the ordinal γ mentioned in Exercise 13.24 is unique.

13.28 Give a counterexample to right cancellation for ordinal addition.

13.29 If $\alpha < \beta$, then $\gamma + \alpha < \gamma + \beta$.

13.30 If $\alpha \leq \beta$, then $\gamma + \alpha \leq \gamma + \beta$.

13.31 If $\gamma + \alpha < \gamma + \beta$, then $\alpha < \beta$.

13.32 If $\gamma + \alpha \leq \gamma + \beta$, then $\alpha \leq \beta$.

13.33 If $\gamma \leq \beta + \gamma$.

13.34 If $\alpha < \beta$, then $\alpha + \gamma \leq \beta + \gamma$.

13.35 Give a counterexample to this statement for ordinals: If $\alpha < \beta$, then $\alpha + \gamma < \beta + \gamma$.

13.36 If $\alpha + \gamma < \beta + \gamma$, then $\alpha < \beta$.

13.37 If $\alpha^+ = \beta^+$, then $\alpha = \beta$.

13.38 If $\alpha < \beta$, then $\alpha + n < \beta + n$ for every natural number n.

13.39 If $\alpha + \alpha = \alpha$, then $\alpha = 0$.

13.40 If $\alpha + \beta = \omega$, then $\alpha\beta = \omega$.

13.41 $\alpha \cdot 0 = 0 \cdot \alpha = 0$.

13.42 $\alpha \cdot 1 = 1 \cdot \alpha = \alpha$.

13.43 Prove the associative law for the multiplication of ordinals.

13.44 Prove that multiplication of ordinals is distributive with respect to addition of ordinals.

13.45 If γ is nonzero and $\alpha < \beta$, then $\gamma\alpha < \gamma\beta$.

13.46 If $\gamma\alpha < \gamma\beta$, then $\alpha < \beta$.

13.47 If γ is nonzero, then $\gamma\alpha = \gamma\beta$ implies $\alpha = \beta$.

13.48 If $\alpha < \beta$, then $\alpha\gamma \leq \beta\gamma$.

13.49 If $\beta\gamma < \alpha\gamma$, then $\beta < \alpha$.

13.50 $\gamma \leq \beta\gamma$ for nonzero β.

13.51 If γ is neither zero nor a limit ordinal and $\alpha < \beta$, then $\alpha\gamma < \beta\gamma$.

13.52 $\alpha\gamma = \beta\gamma$ and γ neither zero nor a limit ordinal imply $\alpha = \beta$.

13.53 If $\alpha\gamma = \beta\gamma$ and $\alpha \neq \beta$, then either $\gamma = 0$ or γ is a limit ordinal.

13.54 Let $\alpha, \beta, \varepsilon$ be ordinals such that $\varepsilon < \alpha\beta$. Then $\varepsilon = \alpha \cdot \beta_1 + \alpha_1$ for some $\alpha_1 < \alpha$, $\beta_1 < \beta$. Moreover, the representation is unique.

13.55 If α, β are ordinals with $\alpha > 0$, then $\beta = \alpha\pi + \rho$ for some ordinals π and ρ, $0 \leq \pi \leq \beta$, $0 \leq \rho < \alpha$. Moreover, the representation is unique.

13.56 A nonzero ordinal β is a limit ordinal if ω is a left factor of β.

13.57 Upon left division by 2, an ordinal has a remainder of 0 or 1. Classify each of the following as odd or even:

a) ω, b) $\omega+1$, c) $1+\omega$, d) $(\omega+1)^2$, e) $(\omega+1)2$.

13.58 Definitions. An ordinal sequence $\alpha = (\alpha_i)_{i \epsilon \mu}$ is a function with domain the ordinal μ and with ordinal values α_i. What role does the axiom of substitution play in this definition? An ordinal sequence $(\alpha_i)_{i \epsilon \mu}$ is an increasing ordinal sequence if $i < j$ implies $\alpha_i \leq \alpha_j$ for all $i, j \epsilon \mu$. By $\lim_{i \epsilon \mu} \alpha_i$ is meant $\sup\{\alpha_i \mid i \epsilon \mu\}$ or in words, the limit of an increasing ordinal sequence is the supremum of the image of the sequence.

Prove that every increasing ordinal sequence has a limit.

13.59 By a neighborhood of the ordinal α we shall mean any open interval (γ, δ) with $\gamma < \alpha$ and $\alpha < \delta$. These are the neighborhoods associated with the order topology; for details one can refer to J. Kelley's *General Topology*, p. 57. An ordinal sequence $(\alpha_i)_{i \epsilon \mu}$ will be said to have a limit λ (with respect to the order topology) iff the ordinal sequence is eventually in every neighborhood of the ordinal λ; that is, given a neighborhood (γ, δ) of λ there exists an ordinal $\nu \epsilon \mu$ such that if $\nu \leq i$, then $\alpha_i \epsilon (\gamma, \delta)$.

Prove that the limit of an increasing ordinal sequence as here defined agrees with the definition $\sup\{\alpha_i \mid i \epsilon \mu\}$ used in Exercise 13.58.

13.60 Prove that a strictly increasing ordinal sequence is a similarity.

13.61 Prove that $(a_i)_{i \in \mu}$ is the only strictly increasing ordinal sequence with μ as index and the same image as $(a_i)_{i \in \mu}$.

13.62 Give an example of two strictly increasing ordinal sequences such that

$$\lim_{i \in \mu} a_i + \lim_{i \in \mu} \beta_i \neq \lim_{i \in \mu} (a_i + \beta_i) \ .$$

13.63 Let Ω be the smallest ordinal which is uncountable (not finite nor equivalent to ω). Prove that if $\alpha \in \Omega$, then α is countable.

13.64 If $A \subset \Omega$ and A is countable, then $\sup A < \Omega$.

13.65 Prove that Ω is an accumulation point of Ω^+, yet no sequence in $\Omega^+ - \{\Omega\}$ (a sequence is an ordinal sequence with index ω) has Ω as a limit. By the sentence "Ω is an accumulation point of Ω^+" is meant that every neighborhood of Ω in Ω^+ contains a member of Ω^+ other than Ω itself. (Cf. Exercise 13.59.)

13.66 Let $(a_i)_{i \in \mu}$ be a strictly increasing ordinal sequence with μ a limit ordinal. Prove that $a_j \neq \lim_{i \in \mu} a_j$ for all $j \in \mu$. Furthermore, $\lim_{i \in \mu} a_i$ is also a limit ordinal.

13.67 Let $(a_i)_{i \in \mu}$ be a strictly increasing ordinal sequence with μ neither 0 nor a limit ordinal. Then prove $\lim_{i \in \mu} a_i$ is the last ordinal in the ordinal sequence. Give an example to illustrate that $\lim_{i \in \mu} a_i$ might possibly be a limit ordinal.

13.68 Let $(a_i)_{i \in \mu}$ be an ordinal sequence with nonzero index, not necessarily an increasing ordinal sequence. Referring to Exercise 13.59 for the meaning of limit, prove that if μ is not a limit ordinal, then $\lim_{i \in \mu} a_i$ exists, and if μ is a limit ordinal, $\lim_{i \in \mu} a_i$ does not always exist.

13.69 For a strictly increasing ordinal sequence $(a_i)_{i \in \mu}$ with nonzero index, prove that $\gamma + \sup\{a_i \mid i \in \mu\} = \sup\{\gamma + a_i \mid i \in \mu\}$.

13.70 For a strictly increasing ordinal sequence $(a_i)_{i \epsilon \mu}$ prove that $\gamma \sup\{a_i \mid i \epsilon \mu\} = \sup\{\gamma a_i \mid i \epsilon \mu\}$.

13.71 Give a counterexample to $\sup\{a_i \mid i \epsilon \mu\} + \gamma = \sup\{a_i + \gamma \mid i \epsilon \mu\}$.

13.72 Give a counterexample to $(\sup\{a_i \mid i \epsilon \mu\}) \gamma = \sup\{a_i \gamma \mid i \epsilon \mu\}$.

13.73 Let $S(x)$ be a condition such that for each ordinal α, $S(\alpha)$ is a statement. If $S(\beta)$ *for every* $\beta < \alpha$ implies $S(\alpha)$, then $S(\alpha)$ for every ordinal α.

13.74 For each ordinal sequence $(a_i)_{i \epsilon \mu}$ let $f((a_i)_{i \epsilon \mu})$ be an ordinal. Then for each ordinal ν there exists a unique ordinal $u(\nu)$ such that $u(\nu) = f(u \mid \nu)$ where $u \mid \nu = \{(\beta, u(\beta)) \mid \beta \epsilon \nu \}$.

13.75 For each ordinal ξ let $g(\xi)$ be an ordinal. Let α be an ordinal. Then for each ordinal ν there exists a unique ordinal $u(\nu)$ such that $u(\nu) = \alpha$ if $\nu = 0$, $u(\nu) = g(u(\beta))$ if $\nu = \beta^+$, $u(\nu) = \sup\{u(\zeta) \mid \zeta < \nu\}$ if ν is a limit ordinal. Furthermore, $u \mid \nu$ is a function.

13.76 For each ordinal β there exists an ordinal $s_\alpha(\beta)$ such that $s_\alpha(\beta) = \alpha$ if $\beta = 0$, $s_\alpha(\beta) = (s_\alpha(\delta))^+$ if $\beta = \delta^+$, $s_\alpha(\beta) = \sup\{s_\alpha(\zeta) \mid \zeta < \beta\}$ if β is a limit ordinal.

13.77 $s_\alpha(\beta) = \alpha + \beta$ for all ordinals β and α.

13.78 For each ordinal β there exists an ordinal $p_\alpha(\beta)$ such that $p_\alpha(\beta) = 0$ if $\beta = 0$, $p_\alpha(\beta) = p_\alpha(\delta) + \alpha$ if $\beta = \delta^+$, $p_\alpha(\beta) = \sup\{p_\alpha(\zeta) \mid \zeta < \beta\}$ if β is a limit ordinal.

13.79 $p_\alpha(\beta) = \alpha\beta$ for all ordinals β and α.

13.80 For each ordinal β there exists an ordinal α^β such that $\alpha^\beta = 1$ if $\beta = 0$, $\alpha^\beta = \alpha^\delta \cdot \alpha$ if $\delta^+ = \beta$, $\alpha^\beta = \sup\{\alpha^\zeta \mid \zeta < \beta\}$ if β is a limit ordinal.

13.81 Associated with an ordinal sequence $(a_i)_{i \epsilon \mu}$ is an ordinal sequence of partial sums $(\Sigma_{i \epsilon k} a_i)_{k \epsilon \mu^+}$ defined as follows:

if $k = 0$, then $\Sigma_{i \epsilon k}\, a_i = 0$; if $k = \delta^+$, then $\Sigma_{i \epsilon k}\, a_i = \Sigma_{i \epsilon \delta}\, a_i + a_\delta$; and if k is a limit ordinal, then $\Sigma_{i \epsilon k}\, a_i = \sup\{\Sigma_{i \epsilon \zeta}\, a_i \mid \zeta < k\}$. The sum of the ordinal sequence $(a_i)_{i \epsilon \mu}$ is the partial sum $\Sigma_{i \epsilon \mu}\, a_i$.

13.82 Let $(a_i)_{i \epsilon \mu}$ be the ordinal sequence such that $a_i = a$ for all $i \epsilon \mu$. Then prove that $\Sigma_{i \epsilon \mu}\, a_i = a\mu$.

13.83 Fine the sum of the ordinal sequence $(a_i)_{i \epsilon \mu}$ where $a_i = \omega$ for all $i \epsilon \mu = \omega$.

13.84 Find the sum of the ordinal sequence $(a_i)_{i \epsilon \mu}$ where $a_i = \omega$ for all $i \epsilon \mu = \omega + 1$.

13.85 Associated with an ordinal sequence $(a_i)_{i \epsilon \mu}$ is an ordinal sequence of partial products $(\Pi_{i \epsilon k}\, a_i)_{k \epsilon \mu^+}$ defined as follows: if $k = 0$, then $\Pi_{i \epsilon k}\, a_i = 1$; if $k = \delta^+$, then $\Pi_{i \epsilon k}\, a_i = \Pi_{i \epsilon \delta}\, a_i \cdot a_\delta$; if k is a limit ordinal, then $\Pi_{i \epsilon k}\, a_i = \sup\{\Pi_{i \epsilon \zeta}\, a_i \mid \zeta < k\}$. The product of the ordinal sequence $(a_i)_{i \epsilon \mu}$ is the partial product $\Pi_{i \epsilon \mu}\, a_i$.

13.86 Let $(a_i)_{i \epsilon \mu}$ be the ordinal sequence such that $a_i = a$ for all $i \epsilon \mu$. Then prove that $\Pi_{i \epsilon \mu}\, a_i = a^\mu$.

13.87 Find the sum and product of the ordinal sequence $(a_i)_{i \epsilon \mu}$ where $a_i = \omega^i$ for all $i \epsilon \mu = \omega$.

13.88 The product of ordinals a_0 and a_1 is defined as the ordinal similar to the set $a_0 \times a_1$ ordered such that $(x_0, x_1) < (y_0, y_1)$ iff $x_1 < y_1$ or ($x_0 < y_0$ and $x_1 = y_1$). Criticize the following generalization. The product of the ordinals $(a_i)_{i \epsilon \mu}$ is the ordinal similar to the set $\mathsf{X}_{i \epsilon \mu}\, a_i$ ordered such that $(x_i)_{i \epsilon \mu} < (y_i)_{i \epsilon \mu}$ iff $x_k < y_k$ for some $k \epsilon \mu$ and $x_i = y_i$ for all $i \epsilon \mu$, $i > k$.

13.89 Let $(a_i)_{i \epsilon \omega}$ be the ordinal sequence defined as follows: $a_0 = \omega$, $a_{\beta+} = (a_\beta)^\omega$. Let $\varepsilon_0 = \sup\{a_i \mid i \epsilon \omega\}$. Prove that $\omega^{\varepsilon_0} = \varepsilon_0$.

CHAPTER 14

CARDINALS

14.0 Schröder-Bernstein Theorem. If $f: X >\!\!\!-\!\!\!> Y$ and $g: Y >\!\!\!-\!\!\!> X$, then there exists an $h: X >\!\!\!-\!\!\!>\!\!> Y$, (NST p88)

Definition of Domination. $X \precsim Y$ iff there exists an $f: X >\!\!\!-\!\!\!> Y$. (NST p87)

Theorem. Domination is reflexive, antisymmetric and transitive. (NST p87)

Cantor's Theorem. $X \prec \mathcal{P}X$ for all sets X. (NST p93) ($\prec$) means ($\precsim$) and not ($\sim$).

Definition of a Cardinal Number. a is a cardinal number iff a is an ordinal number such that if β is an ordinal and $\beta \sim a$, then $a \leq \beta$. The cardinal number of a set X is the least ordinal equivalent to X. (NST p100)

Theorem. card X = card Y iff $X \sim Y$;
card X < card Y iff $X \prec Y$. (NST p100)

Definition. Let a and b be cardinal numbers. Let X and Y be sets so that card $X = a$ and card $Y = b$. Then

$a + b$ = card $X \cup Y$ if $X \cap Y = \emptyset$. (NST p94)

ab = card $X \times Y$. (NST p95)

a^b = card X^Y. (NST p95)

14.1 By definition, X is dominated by Y iff there is an $f: X >\!\!\!-\!\!\!> Y$; X is equivalent to Y iff there is an $f: X >\!\!\!-\!\!\!>\!\!> Y$.

Prove a) domination is reflexive;

b) domination is transitive;

c) domination is antisymmetric;

d) given any set X there exists a set Y which strictly dominates X;

e) any two sets are comparable with respect to domination.

14.2 Prove that ω strictly dominates every $n \in \omega$.

14.3 Using Zorn's lemma, prove that any two sets are comparable with respect to domination. This proof is an alternative proof to the one given on page 89 of NST.

14.4 Prove that $\mathbf{R}$ is equivalent to $(0, 1)$, an open unit interval of $\mathbf{R}$. Prove that $(0, 1)$ is equivalent to $[0, 1)$. Prove that $[0, 1)$ is equivalent to $[0, 1]$.

14.5 If X_1 is equivalent to X_2 and Y_1 is equivalent to Y_2 and $X_1 \cap Y_1 = X_2 \cap Y_2 = \emptyset$, then prove that $X_1 \cup Y_1$ is equivalent to $X_2 \cup Y_2$.

14.6 $A \sim C$ and $B \sim D$ imply $A \times B \sim C \times D$.

14.7 Addition of cardinal numbers is commutative and associative. Multiplication of cardinal numbers is commutative and associative and distributive with respect to addition.

14.8 For cardinal numbers a, b, and c, if $a \leq b$, then $a + c \leq b + c$.

14.9 For cardinal numbers a, b, and c, if $a \leq b$, then $ac \leq bc$.

14.10 For cardinal numbers a, b, show that $ab = \Sigma_{i \in b}\, a$.

14.11 For cardinal numbers a, b, show that $a^b = \Pi_{i \in b}\, a$.

14.12 For cardinal numbers a, b, and c:

$$a^{b+c} = a^b a^c; \quad (ab)^c = a^c b^c; \quad a^{bc} = (a^b)^c .$$

14.13 For cardinal numbers a, b, d, if $a \leq b$, then $a^d \leq b^d$.

14.14 For cardinal numbers a, b; $d \neq 0$, if $a < b$, then $d^a \leq d^b$, and if $d^a < d^b$, then $a < b$.

.15 Every infinite cardinal number is a limit ordinal.

..16 Let $c = 2^{\omega}$. Prove that $1^{\omega} = 1^{c} = 1$. Let $n \in \omega - \{0\}$.
ove that $n + \omega = n\omega = \omega^{n} = \omega + \omega = \omega\omega = \omega$. Furthermore,
$+1)^{\omega} = \omega^{\omega} = n + c = nc = c^{n} = \omega + c = \omega c = c^{\omega} =$
$+ c = cc = c^{2} = c$. And $(n+1)^{c} = \omega^{c} = c^{c} = 2^{c}$.

.17 Let $(a_i)_{i \in I}$ be a nonempty family of cardinal numbers in-
exed by a set I. Let the set $\{a_i \mid i \in I\}$ have no maximum. Then
$_{i \in I} a_i > a_j$ for all $j \in I$.

.18 ω, $2^{\omega} = c$, 2^{c} are distinct cardinal numbers. Prove that
ere exists an infinite set of cardinal numbers (a set of cardinal
umbers does not mean the set of all cardinal numbers).

.19 Prove that there is a unique cardinal number larger than every
ardinal in the family $(\omega, c, 2^{c}, \ldots)$.

.20 If $1 < a \leq d$ and $1 < b \leq d$ for the cardinal numbers a,
d, then $a^{d} = b^{d}$.

.21 Prove that $\omega! = c$ where $\omega!$ means $\Pi_{i \in \omega^{+} - \{0\}}\, i$.

4.22 Prove that $c! = 2^{c}$.

4.23 Prove that every nonfinite cardinal is prime (not the product
f two smaller cardinals).

4.24 Prove that card $\mathbf{Z} = \omega$.

4.25 Prove that card $\mathbf{Q} = \omega$.

4.26 Show that the number of polynomials with rational coefficients
s ω; i.e., card $\mathbf{Q}[X] = \omega$.

4.27 An algebraic number is any root of a polynomial with rational
oefficients. Prove that the number of algebraic numbers is ω.

4.28 Prove that the number of real numbers is 2^{ω}; i.e., card $\mathbf{R} =$
ω.

4.29 What is the cardinality of the set of all continuous functions
rom $\mathbf{R}$ to $\mathbf{R}$?

14.30 Let $B \subset A$ and $\omega \leq$ card $B <$ card A. What is the cardinality of $A - B$?

14.31 It is proven on p. 13 of *Finite Dimensional Vector Spaces* by P. Halmos that if X is a basis for a vector space V with card X = n $(n \; \epsilon \; \omega)$, and if Y is any finite basis for V, then card $Y = n$ also. Prove this generalization of the theorem: If X is a basis for a vector space V and Y is any basis for V, then card $Y =$ card X. Cf. Exercise 10.5 also.

14.32 Prove the existence of an infinite number of infinite cardinal numbers a such that $a < a^\omega$.

14.33 Prove the existence of an infinite number of cardinal numbers β such that $\beta = \beta^\omega$.

14.34 How many groups can be constructed from a set with ω elements?

14.35 Let A have cardinality ω. What is the cardinality of the set of all finite subsets of A?

14.36 Let A have cardinality c. What is the cardinality of the set of all finite subsets of A? countable subsets of A?

14.37 Let A have cardinality 2^e for some cardinal e. Let b be a cardinal $\leq e$. How many subsets of A are there of cardinality $\leq b$?

14.38 Give an example of a set A with cardinality a for which the set of all countable subsets has cardinality greater than a.

14.39 For $f \; \epsilon \; \omega^\omega$ let $s(f) = \{x \,|\, x \; \epsilon \; \omega$ and $f(x) \neq 0\}$. Let $\mathcal{F} = \{f \,|\, f \; \epsilon \; \omega^\omega$ and $s(f)$ is finite $\}$. Prove that $\mathcal{F}$ is countable.

ANSWERS

A1.2 X is not a subset of Y iff there is a member of X not in Y.

A1.3 a) $x \in X$ iff $x \in X$. $X = X$ by the axiom of extension. b) $x \in X$ if and only if $x \in Y$ is equivalent to $x \in Y$ iff $x \in X$. c) ($x \in X$ if and only if $x \in Y$) and ($x \in Y$ if and only if $x \in Z$) imply ($x \in X$ if and only if $x \in Z$).

A1.4 a) $x \in X$ implies $x \in X$. b) (If $x \in X$, then $x \in Y$), and (if $x \in Y$, then $x \in X$) imply ($x \in X$ iff $x \in Y$). c) (If $x \in X$, then $x \in Y$) and (if $x \in Y$, then $x \in Z$) imply (if $x \in X$, then $x \in Z$).

A1.5 Let $c \in C$ and $c \notin B$. This is possible since B is a proper subset of C. $c \notin A$, because if $c \in A$, then $c \in B$.

A1.6 To prove that $A = B$ one need only prove every member of B to be a member of A. Every member of B is a member of C and every member of C is a member of A.

A1.7 (If p then q) is equivalent to (if not q then not p) and (not (not p)) is equivalent to p.

A1.8 The statement (if $x \in \emptyset$, then $x \in P$) must be demonstrated true. If this statement were false, then there would exist a y such that $y \in \emptyset$ and $y \notin P$. But this cannot be since $y \notin \emptyset$. Thus $\emptyset \subset P$.

A1.9 P and Q are sets imply $\{P, Q\}$ is a set by the axiom of pairing, which in turn implies $\bigcup\{P, Q\}$ is a set by the axiom of union and specification.

A1.10 ($x \in X$ or $x \in \emptyset$) is equivalent to ($x \in X$), since ($x \in \emptyset$) is always false.

A1.11 If $X \cup Y = X$ for all sets X, then $\emptyset \cup Y = \emptyset$. But $\emptyset \cup Y = Y$. Therefore $Y = \emptyset$.

A1.12 ($x \in X$ and $x \in \emptyset$) is equivalent to ($x \in \emptyset$), since ($x \in \emptyset$) is always false.

A1.13 The solutions probably come most easily by utilizing the equivalences of 1.1: a) 1.1*j*, b) 1.1*i*, c) 1.1*o*, d) 1.1*n*, e) 1.1*k*, f) 1.1*ℓ*, g) 1.1*q* h) 1.1*p*.

A1.14 Let A be a set. $0 = \emptyset = \{x \mid x \in A \text{ and } x \neq x\}$ is a set by the axiom of specification. $\{0\}$ is a set by the axiom of pairing. $\{0, \{0\}\}$ is a set by the axiom of pairing. $1 = \bigcup \{0, \{0\}\}$ is a set by the axiom of union and specification. The same argument repeats with 1, 2, 3, 4 successively replacing 0.

A1.15 $4 = \{\emptyset, \{\emptyset\}, \{\emptyset, \{\emptyset\}\}, \{\emptyset, \{\emptyset\}, \{\emptyset, \{\emptyset\}\}\}\}$.

A1.16 Only c) is false.

A1.17 The proof is similar to that in 1.14.

A1.18 x is a member: D, E, F. x is a subset: B, E. x is neither a member nor a subset: A, C. The members of the set x are not given here and the answers are on the basis that $x \notin x$.

A1.20 0, 0, 1, 0, 2, 0, $\{0, 1, 2, \{1\}\}$.

A1.21 4.

A1.22 $\{1, 2\}$.

A1.23 1.

A1.24 $\{\{1, 2\}, \{1\}, \{1, 0\}\}$, 0, 3, not defined, 0, $\{1\}$.

A1.25 4, 0, 3, not defined, 0, 0.

A1.26 Exercise 1.1 contains suitable equivalences.

A1.27 The statement ($x \in A$ or $x \in B$ iff $x \in A$) is equivalent to the statement ($x \in B$ implies $x \in A$), which may be easily verified with a truth table.

A1.28 ($x \in A$ and $x \in B$ iff $x \in A$) is an equivalent statement to ($x \in A$ implies $x \in B$).

A1.29 For example, $A = \{1\}$, $B = \{0, 1\}$.

A1.30 $x \in (\bigcap A) \cap (\bigcap B)$ implies $x \in (\bigcap A)$ and $x \in (\bigcap B)$. Which implies $x \in (\bigcap A)$. Which implies for all $X \in A$ one has $x \in X$. Which implies for all X if $X \in A$ and $X \in B$ then $x \in X$. Which implies for all $X \in A \cap B$ one has $x \in X$. Which in turn implies $x \in \bigcap(A \cap B)$.

A1.31 $\{1, 2\} \notin \mathcal{P}\{0, 1\} \cup \mathcal{P}\{0, 2\}$. $\{1, 2\} \in \mathcal{P}\{0, 1, 2\}$.

A1.32 $(\sqrt{2}, \infty)$

A1.34 $\{x \mid x \in \mathcal{P}A$ and $x = A\}$ is a set using the power axiom and specification.

A2.1 a) 3, b) 2, c) $\{(0, 0), (0, 1), (0, 2), (1, 0), (1, 1), (1, 2)\}$ d) $\{(0, 0), (1, 0)\}$, e) $\{(0, 0), (0, 1)\}$, f) 0 g) $\{(0, 0)\}$.

A2.2 If $x = b$ and $y = a$ and $a \neq b$, then $\{x, y\} = \{a, b\}$ and $x \neq a$ and $y \neq b$.

A2.3 The ordered pair (x, x) has only the member $\{x\}$.

A2.4 If $X = \{0\}$ and $Y = \{1\}$, then $X \times Y \neq Y \times X$ because $(0, 1) \neq (1, 0)$. $0 \neq 1$ because $0 \in 1$ and $0 \notin 0$.

A2.5 If $X = \{0\}$, $Y = \{0\}$, $Z = \{1\}$, then $(X \times Y) \times Z \neq X \times (Y \times Z)$. $(X \times Y) \times Z = \{((0, 0), 1)\}$; $X \times (Y \times Z) = \{(0, (0, 1))\}$. $(0, 0) \neq 0$.

A2.6 Let either set be $\emptyset$.

A2.7 $(x, y) \in X \times (Y \cup Z)$ iff $x \in X$, and $y \in Y \cup Z$ iff $x \in X$ and ($y \in Y$ or $y \in Z$) iff ($x \in X$ and $y \in Y$) or ($x \in X$ and $y \in Z$) iff $(x, y) \in X \times Y$ or $(x, y) \in X \times Z$ iff $(x, y) \in (X \times Y) \cup (X \times Z)$.

A2.8 $X = 1$, $Y = Z = 0$.

A2.9 $a \in \bigcap\{\{x\}, \{x, y\}\}$ iff $a \in \{x\}$ and $a \in \{x, y\}$ if $a = x$ and $(a = x$ or $a = y)$ iff $a = x$.

A2.10 Prove first $\bigcup(x, y) = \{x, y\}$. Then $a \in (\bigcap\{x, y\}) \cup (\bigcup\{x, y\} - \bigcup\{x\})$ iff $(a \in x$ and $a \in y)$ or $((a \in x$ or $a \in y)$ and $a \notin x)$ iff $(a \in x$ and $a \in y)$ or $a \in y$ iff $a \in y$.

A2.11 Let $x \in X$. Then $(x, x) \in X \times X$. $(x, x) \in Y \times Y$. $x \in Y$. $X \subset Y$. Likewise $Y \subset X$. $X = Y$.

A2.12 Let $y \in Y$. Since $X \neq \emptyset$ let $a \in X$. Then $(a, y) \in X \times Y$. $(a, y) \in X \times Z$. $y \in Z$. Likewise $Z \subset Y$. $Y = Z$.

A3.1 $X \times Y$, $\{(a, s), (b, s)\}$, $\{(a, s), (c, s)\}$, $\{(b, s), (c, s)\}$, $\{(a, s)\}$, $\{(b, s)\}$, $\{(c, s)\}$, $\emptyset$.

A3.2 $\emptyset$ and 1×1.

A3.3 2^{n^2}.

A3.4 $(w, z) \in T \circ (S \circ R)$ iff $(w, y) \in S \circ R$ and $(y, z) \in T$ for some $y \in Y$ iff $((w, x) \in R$ and $(x, y) \in S$ for some $x \in X)$ and $(y, z) \in T$ for some $y \in Y$ iff $(w, z) \in R$ and $((x, y) \in S$ and $(y, z) \in T$ for some $y \in Y)$ for some $x \in X$ iff $(w, x) \in R$ and $(x, z) \in T \circ S$ for some $x \in X$ iff $(w, z) \in (T \circ S) \circ R$.

A3.5 As $Y \times X$ and S are sets, $S^{-1} = \{(y, x) | (y, x) \in Y \times X$ and $(x, y) \in S\}$ is a set by the axiom of specification. S^{-1} is a relation from Y to X because it is a subset of $Y \times X$.

A3.6 Let $(x, y) \in S$. Then $y \in Y$ and therefore $(y, y) \in I_Y$. Then $(x, y) \in I_Y \circ S$. Now on the other hand, let $(x, y) \in I_Y \circ S$. $(x, z) \in S$ and $(z, y) \in I_Y$ for some $z \in Y$. But $(z, y) \in I_Y$ yields $z = y$. $z = y$ implies $(x, y) \in S$. The second equation is proven with a similar argument.

A3.7 $y \in S(A)$ implies $(x, y) \in S$ for some $x \in A$ which implies $y \in Y$. $z \in (T \circ S)(A)$ iff $(x, z) \in T \circ S$ for some $x \in A$ iff

$(x, y) \in S$ and $(y, z) \in T$ for some $y \in Y$ and $x \in A$ iff $(y, z) \in T$ for some $y \in S(A)$ iff $z \in T(S(A))$.

$y \in S(A) \cup S(B)$ implies $y \in S(A)$ or $y \in S(B)$ which implies $(x_1, y) \in S$ for some $x_1 \in A$ or $(x_2, y) \in S$ for some $x_2 \in B$ which implies $(x_1, y) \in S$ for some $x_1 \in A \cup B$ or $(x_2, y) \in S$ for some $x_2 \in A \cup B$ which implies $y \in S(A \cup B)$.

$y \in S(A \cup B)$ implies $(x, y) \in S$ for some $x \in A \cup B$. If $x \in A$, then $(x, y) \in S$ for some $x \in A$ yielding $y \in S(A)$. If on the other hand $x \in B$, then $(x, y) \in S$ for some $x \in B$ yielding $y \in S(B)$. In either case $y \in S(A) \cup S(B)$.

$y \in S(A \cap B)$ implies $(x, y) \in S$ for some $x \in A \cap B$ which implies $x \in A$ and $x \in B$ and $(x, y) \in S$ for some $x \in X$ which implies $y \in S(A)$ and $y \in S(B)$ which implies $y \in S(A) \cap S(B)$.

A3.8 $(y, x) \in (S \cap T)^{-1}$ iff $(x, y) \in S \cap T$ iff $(x, y) \in S$ and $(x, y) \in T$ iff $(y, x) \in S^{-1}$ and $(y, x) \in T^{-1}$ iff $(y, x) \in S^{-1} \cap T^{-1}$. Similarly for $\cup$.

A3.9 $(z, x) \in (T \cdot S)^{-1}$ iff $(x, z) \in T \circ S$ iff $(x, y) \in S$ and $(y, z) \in T$ for some $y \in Y$ iff $(z, y) \in T^{-1}$ and $(y, x) \in S^{-1}$ for some $y \in Y$ iff $(z, x) \in S^{-1} \circ T^{-1}$.

A3.10 Let S be reflexive. Let $(x, y) \in I_X$. Then $x = y$. But $(x, x) \in S$ because S is reflexive. Hence $(x, y) = (x, x) \in S$. $I_X \subset S$. Let $I_x \subset S$ to prove the converse. Let $x \in X$. $(x, x) \in I_X$. But $I_X \subset S$. Therefore $(x, x) \in S$ and S is reflexive.

S is irreflexive iff $(x, x) \notin S$ for all $x \in X$ iff $(x, x) \notin S$ for all $(x, x) \in I_X$ iff $S \cap I_X = \emptyset$.

Let S be transitive. If $(x, z) \in S \circ S$, then $(x, y) \in S$ and $(y, z) \in S$ for some $y \in X$. But if S is transitive, then $(x, z) \in S$. $S \circ S \subset S$. Conversely let $S \circ S \subset S$. Assume $(x, y) \in S$ and $(y, z) \in S$. Then $(x, z) \in S \circ S$. Since $S \circ S \subset S$ also $(x, z) \in S$. S is transitive.

Let S be atransitive. Let $(x, z) \in S \circ S$. Then $(x, y) \in S$ and $(y, z) \in S$ for some $y \in X$. Therefore $(x, z) \notin S$. $(S \circ S) \cap S = \emptyset$. Conversely, let $(S \circ S) \cap S = \emptyset$. Let $(x, y) \in S$ and $(y, z) \in S$. $(x, z) \in S \circ S$. $(x, z) \notin S$.

S is symmetric iff ($(x, y) \in S$ implies $(y, x) \in S$) iff ($(x, y) \in S$ implies $(y, x) \in S^{-1}$) iff $S \subset S^{-1}$ iff $S = S^{-1}$.

Let S be antisymmetric. Assume $(x, y) \in S \cap S^{-1}$. Then $(x, y) \in S$ and $(x, y) \in S^{-1}$. $(y, x) \in S$. By antisymmetry $x = y$. $(x, y) = (x, x) \in I_X$. Conversely, let $S \cap S^{-1} \subset I_X$. Let $(x, y) \in S$ and $(y, x) \in S$. Then $(x, y) \in S$ and $(x, y) \in S^{-1}$. $(x, y) \in S \cap S^{-1}$. $(x, y) \in I_X$. $x = y$.

A3.11 If S is transitive, then $S \circ S \subset S$. Let $(x, y) \in S$. By reflexivity, $(x, x) \in S$. Therefore $(x, y) \in S \circ S$. $S \subset S \circ S$. No, the converse is not true. Example: $X = 1$ and $S = 0$.

A3.12 It is perhaps simpler to construct the partitions of 3 first, then the corresponding equivalence relations. The partitions of $3 = \{0, 1, 2\}$ are

$$\{\{0\}, \{1\}, \{2\}\}, \quad \{\{0, 1\}, \{2\}\} \quad \{\{0, 2\}, \{1\}\}, \quad \{\{1, 2\}, \{0\}\}, \quad \{\{0, 1, 2\}\}.$$

The corresponding equivalence relations are I_3, $I_3 \cup \{(0, 1), (1, 0)\}$, $I_3 \cup \{(2, 0), (0, 2)\}$, $I_3 \cup \{(1, 2), (2, 1)\}$, 3×3.

A3.13 Let $S \in \bigcap \mathcal{S} \neq \emptyset$. Then $\bigcap \mathcal{S} \subset S \subset X \times X$. Let $x \in X$. Then $(x, x) \in S$ for all $S \in \mathcal{S}$. Therefore $(x, x) \in \bigcap \mathcal{S}$. Let $(x, y) \in \bigcap \mathcal{S}$. $(x, y) \in S$ for all $S \in \mathcal{S}$. $(y, x) \in S$ for all $S \in \mathcal{S}$. $(y, x) \in \bigcap \mathcal{S}$. Now let (x, y) and $(y, z) \in \bigcap \mathcal{S}$. (x, y) and $(y, z) \in S$ for all $S \in \mathcal{S}$. $(x, z) \in S$ for all $S \in \mathcal{S}$. $(x, z) \in \bigcap \mathcal{S}$

A3.14 Equality $= \{(A, B) | (A, B) \in \mathcal{P}X \times \mathcal{P}X$ and $A = B\}$. [Cf. 1.3 for the rest of the proof.]

A3.15 There are nineteen orders on 3:

I_3,	$I_3 \cup \{(0, 1)\}$,	$I_3 \cup \{(0, 2)\}$,
$I_3 \cup \{(1, 2)\}$,	$I_3 \cup \{(1, 0)\}$,	$I_3 \cup \{(2, 0)\}$,

$I_3 \cup \{(2, 1)\}$,
$I_3 \cup \{(0, 1), (2, 0), (2, 1)\}$,
$I_3 \cup \{(0, 1), (2, 1)\}$,
$I_3 \cup \{(1, 0), (2, 0)\}$,
$I_3 \cup \{(1, 0), (2, 1), (2, 0)\}$,
$I_3 \cup \{(2, 0), (2, 1)\}$,
$I_3 \cup \{(0, 2), (2, 1), (0, 1)\}$.
$I_3 \cup \{(0, 1), (0, 2)\}$.
$I_3 \cup \{(0, 1), (1, 2), (0, 2)\}$,
$I_3 \cup \{(1, 0), (0, 2), (1, 2)\}$,
$I_3 \cup \{(1, 0), (1, 2)\}$,
$I_3 \cup \{(2, 0), (1, 2), (1, 0)\}$,
$I_3 \cup \{(0, 2), (1, 2)\}$,

The orders with six elements are total orders.

A3.16 Since both orders and equivalence relations are reflexive relations, the only possible set on which $\emptyset$ could be an order or an equivalence relation is $\emptyset$ itself. That it is an order and an equivalence relation is easily verified.

A3.17 The proof is analogous to the proof in Exercise 3.13.

A3.18 Cf. Exercise 1.3.

A3.19 Let S be an order on X. $S \cap (A \times A) \subset A \times A$. Let $x \in A$. $(x, x) \in S$ and $(x, x) \in A \times A$. $(x, x) \in S \cap (A \times A)$.

Let $(x, y) \in S \cap (A \times A)$ and $(y, x) \in S \cap (A \times A)$. $(x, y) \in S$ and $(y, x) \in S$. $x = y$.

Let $(x, y) \in S \cap (A \times A)$ and $(y, z) \in S \cap (A \times A)$. $(x, y) \in S$ and $(y, z) \in S$. $(x, z) \in S$. $(x, y) \in A \times A$ and $(y, z) \in A \times A$. Therefore $x, y, z \in A$. $(x, z) \in A \times A$. $(x, z) \in S \cap (A \times A)$. Therefore $S \cap (A \times A)$ is an order on A.

Let S be total on X. Let $x, y \in A$. Then $(x, y) \in S$ or $(y, x) \in S$. But $(x, y) \in A \times A$ and $(y, x) \in A \times A$. Therefore (x, y) or $(y, x) \in S \cap (A \times A)$.

A3.20 Utilizing the conditions of Exercise 3.10, S^{-1} is an order iff $S^{-1} \subset X \times X$ and $I_X \subset S^{-1}$ and $S^{-1} \cap S^{-1} \subset S^{-1}$ and $S^{-1} \cap (S^{-1})^{-1} \subset I_X$. These are readily verifiable.

A3.21 a) $S = \{(0, 0), (0, 1), (0, 2), (0, 3), (0, 4), (0, 5), (0, 6), (0, 7),$
$(1, 1), (1, 2), (1, 3), (1, 4), (1, 5), (1, 6), (1, 7), (2, 2),$
$(2, 3), (2, 4), (2, 5), (2, 6), (2, 7), (3,3), (3, 4), (3, 5),$

(3, 6), (3, 7), (4, 4), (4, 5), (4, 6), (4, 7), (5, 5), (5, 6), (5, 7), (6, 6), (6, 7), (7, 7),}.

b) $S - I_8$, c) I_8,

d) $I_8 \cup \{(0, 2), (0, 4), (0, 6), (2, 0), (2, 4), (2, 6), (4, 0), (4, 2), (4, 6), (6, 0), (6, 2), (6, 4), (1, 3), (1, 5), (1, 7), (3, 1), (3, 5), (3, 7), (5, 1), (5, 3), (5, 7), (7, 1), (7, 3), (7, 5)\}$.

e) {(5, 0), (6, 0), (7, 0), (6, 1), (7, 1), (7, 2),}.

f) {(0, 1), (1, 2), (2, 3), (3, 4), (4, 5), (5, 6), (6, 7)}.

Symmetric: *c*, *d*. Antisymmetric: *a*, *b*, *c*, *e*, *f*.
Reflexive: *a*, *c*, *d*. Irreflexive: *b*, *e*, *f*.
Transitive: *a*, *b*, *c*, *d*, *e*. Atransitive: *f*.
Orders: *a*, *c*. Equivalence relations: *c*, *d*.
For c: $\{\{0\}, \{1\}, \{2\}, \{4\}, \{5\}, \{6\}, \{7\}\}$.
For *d*: $\{\{0, 2, 4, 6\}, \{1, 3, 5, 7\}\}$.

A3.23 $(\prec) \subset A \times A$. $f \not\prec f$ because $f = qf$ with $\deg q \geq 1$ gives a contradiction. Note that $Q[X] - Q$ consists of polynomials of degree ≥ 1. Suppose that $f \prec g$ and $g \prec f$. $g = q_1 f$ and $f = q_2 g$ yields $g = q_1 q_2 g$ and $\deg g > \deg g$ which is a contradiction. Now suppose $f \prec g$ and $g \prec h$. $g = q_1 f$ and $h = q_2 g$. Then $h = (q_2 q_1) f$ with $\deg q_2 q_1 = \deg q_2 + \deg q_1 \geq 2$. The order is not total. For example, the following polynomials are not comparable: $x^2 + 1$, $x + 1$, x.

A3.24 Let S be an order on X and consider $S - I_X$. $S - I_X \subset X \times X$, for $S \subset X \times X$. Let $x \in X$. $(x, x) \in I_X$ and therefore $(x, x) \notin S - I_X$. Let (x, y) and $(y, x) \in S - I_X$. Then $(x, y) \in S$ and $(y, x) \in S$ imply $x = y$. Now let (x, y) and $(y, z) \in S - I_X$. It follows that $(x, z) \in S$. Then $(x, z) \in S - I_X$ unless $x = z$. If $x = z$, then (x, y) and (y, x) both belong to S, yielding $x = y$. But $(x, y) \in S - I_X$ implies $x \neq y$ giving a contradiction.

A3.25 $\emptyset$ is a strict order on any set X.

A3.26 It must be shown that $S \subset (\bigcup\bigcup S \times \bigcup\bigcup S)$.

$\alpha \in \bigcup S$ iff $\alpha \in (x, y)$ for some $(x, y) \in S$,
iff $\alpha \in \{\{x\}, \{x, y\}\}$ for some $(x, y) \in S$,
iff $\alpha = \{x\}$ or $\alpha = \{x, y\}$ for some $(x, y) \in S$.

$\beta \in \bigcup\bigcup S$ iff $\beta \in \alpha$ for some $\alpha \in \bigcup S$,
iff $\beta \in \{x\}$ or $\beta \in \{x, y\}$ for some $(x, y) \in S$,
iff $\beta = x$ or $\beta = y$ for some $(x, y) \in S$.

Now if $(x, y) \in S$, we have $x \in \bigcup\bigcup S$ and $y \in \bigcup\bigcup S$, yielding $(x, y) \in \bigcup\bigcup S \times \bigcup\bigcup S$.

Let $\beta \in \bigcup\bigcup S$. Then $\beta = x$ of some $(x, y) \in S \subset X \times X$ or $\beta = y$ of some $(x, y) \in S \subset X \times X$. Therefore $\beta \in X$.

A3.27 $x \in$ preimage S implies $(x, y) \in S \subset X \times Y$. $x \in X$. $y \in$ image S implies $(x, y) \in S \subset X \times Y$. $y \in Y$.

A3.28 Let $x \in$ preimage S. There exists an $(x, y) \in S$. Hence $(y, x) \in S^{-1}$. $(x, x) \in S^{-1} \circ S$.

Let $y \in$ image S. There exists an $(x, y) \in S$. $(y, x) \in S^{-1}$. $(y, y) \in S \circ S^{-1}$.

A3.29 $P \subset (X \times Y) \times (X \times Y)$. Let $(x, y) \in X \times Y$. $x \in X$ and $y \in Y$. $(x, x) \in S$ and $(y, y) \in T$. $((x, y), (x, y)) \in P$. P is reflexive. Now let $((x_1, y_1), (x_2, y_2)) \in P$ and $((x_2, y_2), (x_1, y_1)) \in P$. Then $(x_1, x_2) \in S$ and $(y_1, y_2) \in T$ and $(x_2, x_1) \in S$ and $(y_2, y_1) \in T$. $x_1 = x_2$ and $y_1 = y_2$. $(x_1, y_1) = (x_2, y_2)$. P is antisymmetric. Now let $((x_1, y_1), (x_2, y_2)) \in P$ and $((x_2, y_2), (x_3, y_3)) \in P$. $(x_1, x_2) \in S$ and $(y_1, y_2) \in T$ and $(x_2, x_3) \in S$ and $(y_2, y_3) \in T$. Therefore $(x_1, x_3) \in S$ and $(y_1, y_3) \in T$. $((x_1, y_1), (x_3, y_3)) \in P$.

A3.30 Similar to 3.29.

A3.31 $R = \{((x_1, y_1), (x_2, y_2)) | (y_1, y_2) \in T$ or $[(x_1, x_2) \in S$ and $y_1 = y_2]\}$ is a set using the axiom of specification on $(X \times Y) \times (X \times Y)$. R is irreflexive since $((x_1, y_1), (x_2, y_2)) \in R$ implies $(y_1, y_2) \in T$ with $y_1 \neq y_2$ or it implies $(x_1, x_2) \in S$ with $x_1 \neq x_2$. In either case $(x_1, y_1) \neq (x_2, y_2)$. Now for antisymmetry assume both $((x_1, y_1), (x_2, y_2)) \in R$ and $((x_2, y_2), (x_1, y_1)) \in R$. The four cases all yield $(x_1, y_1) = (x_2, y_2)$. Transitivity follows similarly.

A3.32 Let F be the set of all partitions of X. S is finer than S because $u \in S$ implies $u \subset u$ for some $u \in S$. Suppose S finer than T and T finer than S. $u \in S$ implies $u \subset v$ for some $v \in T$. $v \in T$ implies there is a $u' \in S$ such that $v \subset u'$. Either $u' = u$ or $u' \cap u = \emptyset$ because S is a partition. Since $u \neq \emptyset$ let $a \in u$. Then $a \in v$. $a \in u'$. $u' \cap u \neq \emptyset$. Therefore $u = u'$ and we have $u = v$. $S \subset T$. Similarly, $T \subset S$, and we conclude that $S = T$. Let S be finer than T and T finer than U. Let $u \in S$. $u \subset v$ for some $v \in T$. $v \subset w$ for some $w \in U$. Thus S is finer than U, since for each $u \in S$ there exists a $w \in U$ such that $u \subset w$.

A3.33 Let $X = 2$ and $\mathcal{S} = \{\{(0, 0), (0, 1), (1, 1)\}, \{(0, 0), (1, 0), (1, 1)\}\}$ for example. $\bigcup \mathcal{S} = X \times X = 2 \times 2$, which is not an order.

A3.34 Let R be a relation on X. Let $\mathcal{S}$ be the set of all symmetric relations on X, each included in R. $\bigcup \mathcal{S}$ is a symmetric relation, for suppose $(x, y) \in \bigcup \mathcal{S}$. Then $(x, y) \in S$ for some $S \in \mathcal{S}$. $(y, x) \in S \subset \bigcup \mathcal{S}$. $\bigcup \mathcal{S} \in \mathcal{S}$. $\bigcup \mathcal{S} \subset R$ and is the largest symmetric relation included in R.

Now it will be proven that $\bigcup \mathcal{S} = R \cap R^{-1}$. Let $(x, y) \in R \cap R^{-1}$. $(x, y) \in R$ and $(x, y) \in R^{-1}$. $(y, x) \in R^{-1}$ and $(y, x) \in R$. $(y, x) \in R \cap R^{-1}$. $R \cap R^{-1} \subset R$. $R \cap R^{-1} \in \mathcal{S}$. $R \cap R^{-1} \subset \bigcup \mathcal{S}$. Suppose that $(x, y) \in \bigcup \mathcal{S}$. Then $(x, y) \in S$ for some $S \in \mathcal{S}$. $(y, x) \in S$. (x, y) and $(y, x) \in S$. $S \subset R$. (x, y) and $(y, x) \in R$. $(x, y) \in R \cap R^{-1}$. $\bigcup \mathcal{S} \subset R \cap R^{-1}$.

Let $\mathcal{S} = \{S \mid S$ is a symmetric relation on X and $R \subset S\}$. $X \times X \in \mathcal{S}$. $\mathcal{S} \neq \emptyset$. Define $s(R) = \bigcap \mathcal{S}$. $s(R)$ is the smallest symmetric relation which includes R. Why?

Now it will be proven that $s(R) = R \cup R^{-1}$. First prove $R \cup R^{-1}$ symmetric. $(x, y) \in R \cup R^{-1}$ implies $(x, y) \in R$ or $(y, x) \in R$ which implies $(y, x) \in R^{-1}$ or $(y, x) \in R$ which implies $(y, x) \in R \cup R^{-1}$.

Thus $R \cup R^{-1} \in \mathcal{S}$ so $s(R) \subset R \cup R^{-1}$. Let T be any symmetric relation which includes R. Suppose $(x, y) \in R \cup R^{-1}$. If $(x, y) \in R$, then $(x, y) \in T$. If $(x, y) \in R^{-1}$, then $(y, x) \in R$. $(y, x) \in T$. $(x, y) \in T$. Hence $R \cup R^{-1} \subset T$ for all $T \in \mathcal{S}$. $R \cup R^{-1} \subset s(R)$.

A3.35 Define $(x, y) \in S$ iff $(x, y) \in R$ and $(y, x) \in R$. That S is an equivalence relation follows thus: $(x, x) \in S$ since $(x, x) \in R$. $(x, y) \in S$ implies $(x, y) \in R$ and $(y, x) \in R$ which implies $(y, x) \in R$ and $(x, y) \in R$ which implies $(y, x) \in S$. Finally $(x, y) \in S$ and $(y, z) \in S$ implies $(x, y) \in R$ and $(y, x) \in R$ and $(y, z) \in R$ and $(z, y) \in R$ which implies $(x, z) \in R$ and $(z, x) \in R$ which implies $(x, z) \in S$.

$\bar{R}$ as defined is clearly a subset of $X/S \times X/S$. That the relation is well defined is now checked. Let $x'/S = x/S$ and $y'/S = y/S$. $(x/S, y/S) \in \bar{R}$ implies $(x, y) \in R$. But $(x', x) \in S$ implies $(x', x) \in R$ and $(x, x') \in R$. $(y', y) \in S$ implies $(y', y) \in R$ and $(y, y') \in R$. $(x', y') \in R$. $(x'/S, y'/S) \in \bar{R}$. That $\bar{R}$ is an order is verified now. $(x, x) \in R$ implies $(x/S, x/S) \in \bar{R}$. $(x/S, y/S) \in \bar{R}$ and $(y/S, x/S) \in \bar{R}$ implies $(x, y) \in R$ and $(y, x) \in R$ which implies $(x, y) \in S$ which implies $x/S = y/S$. $(x/S, y/S) \in \bar{R}$ and $(y/S, z/S) \in \bar{R}$ implies (x, y) and $(y, z) \in R$ which implies $(x, z) \in R$ which implies $(x/S, z/S) \in \bar{R}$.

A4.1 For example, a) $\{(n, 0) | n \in \mathbf{N}\}$, b) $\{(n, n+1) | n \in \mathbf{N}\}$, c) $\{(n, 0) | n \in \mathbf{Z}\}$, d) $\{(n, 2n) | n \in \mathbf{Z}\}$, e) $\{(x, 0) | x \in \mathbf{R}\}$, f) $\{(x, 0) | x \in \mathbf{R} - \{0\}\} \cup \{(0, 1)\}$.

A4.2 See A 4.1 b).

A4.3 a) $\{(0,0)\}$, b) $\emptyset$, c) one bijection from 2×3 to 6 is $\{((0, 0), 0), ((0, 1), 1), ((0, 2), 2), ((1, 0), 3), ((1, 1), 4), ((1, 2), 5)\}$.

A4.4 a) $\{\{(0,0),(1,0),(2,0)\}, \{(0,0),(1,0),(2,1)\},$
$\{(0,0),(1,1),(2,0)\}, \{(0,0),(1,1),(2,1)\},$
$\{(0,1),(1,0),(2,0)\}, \{(0,1),(1,0),(2,1)\},$
$\{(0,1),(1,1),(2,0)\}, \{(0,1),(1,1),(2,1)\}\}$.

b) $\{\{(0,0),(1,0)\}, \{(0,1),(1,0)\}, \{(0,2),(1,0)\},$
$\{(0,0),(1,1)\}, \{(0,1),(1,1)\}, \{(0,2),(1,1)\},$
$\{(0,0),(1,2)\}, \{(0,1),(1,2)\}, \{(0,2),(1,2)\}\}$.

c) $\{\emptyset\} = 1$ d) 0, e) 1, f) 1, g) $\{\{(0,0)\}\}$, h) 0,
i) $\{\{(0,0)\}, \{(0,1)\}\}$, j) $\{\{(0,0), (1,0)\}\}$.

A4.5 If $X = \emptyset$ then $f = \emptyset$, which is injective, because if $(x_1, y) \in \emptyset$ and $(x_2, y) \in \emptyset$, then $x_1 = x_2$. If $Y = \emptyset$ and f is a function from X to Y, then $X = \emptyset$ also and $f = \emptyset$, which is again an injection.

A4.6 If $Y = \emptyset$ and f is a function, then f is a surjection.

A4.7 $\{(0,0), (1,1), (\{1\},2), (2,3)\}$ is a bijection.

A4.8 First let $A = 0$ and $B \neq 0$. $f \in A^B$ implies $f \subset B \times 0 = 0$. But 0 is not a function from $B \neq 0$ to $A = 0$. Therefore $A^B = 0$. For the converse, suppose $A \neq 0$. Let a be an element of A. Then $\{(x, a) | x \in B\}$ is a function from B to A giving $A^B \neq 0$. If on the other hand $B = 0$, then 0 is a function from B to A and again $A^B \neq 0$.

A4.9 If $X^Y \neq \emptyset$ let $f \in X^Y = Y^X$. Then domain $f = Y$, since $f \in X^Y$. But domain $f = X$, since $f \in Y^X$. $X = Y$. If on the other hand $X^Y = 0$, then by 4.8 $X = 0$. But $Y^X = 0$ also yielding $Y = 0$. Again $X = Y$.

A4.10 Let $f \in A^C$. Then observe 0) $f \subset C \times A \subset C \times B$, 1) for all $x \in C$ there exists a $y \in A$ (and therefore $y \in B$) such that $(x, y) \in f$, 2) $(x, y_1) \in f$ and $(x, y_2) \in f$ imply $y_1 = y_2$. f is therefore a function from C to B and therefore is a member of B^C.

A4.11 Let $\phi: A \rightarrowtail\!\!\twoheadrightarrow B$. Let $f \in A^C$. Then define $\Phi: A^C \rightarrowtail\!\!\twoheadrightarrow$

Let $f \in A^C$. Then define $\Phi: A^C \rightarrowtail\!\!\twoheadrightarrow B^C$ as follows: $\Phi(f) = \phi \circ f$. Φ is injective, since $\phi \circ f = \phi \circ g$ implies $f = g$. Cf. 4.29. Φ is surjective, since for $g \in B^C$ $\Phi(\phi^{-1} \circ g) = \phi \circ \phi^{-1} \circ g = g$.

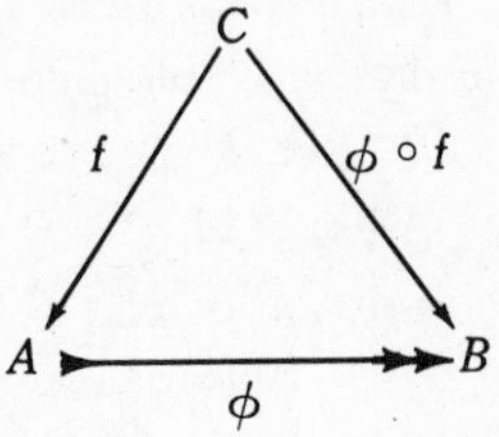

A4.12 To prove $f = I_X$ it remains to prove $I_X \subset f$. Let $x \in X$. Since f is a function, $(x, y) \in f$ for some $y \in X$. But $f \subset I_X$ is given. $(x, y) \in I_X$. $x = y$. $(x, x) \in f$. Therefore $I_X \subset f$.

A4.13 Given $I_X \subset f$, it remains to prove that $f \subset I_X$. Let $(x, y) \in f$. Then $x \in X$. $(x, x) \in I_X$. $(x, x) \in f$ since $I_X \subset f$. $(x, x) \in f$ and $(x, y) \in f$ imply $x = y$. Therefore $(x, y) = (x, x) \in I_X$. $f \subset I_X$.

A4.14 If $n = 1$ then $f = I_X$, which is a bijection. Assume now that $n > 1$. Suppose f is not an injection. $f(x_1) = f(x_2)$ for some $x_1, x_2 \in X$, $x_1 \neq x_2$. $f^{n-1}f(x_1) = f^{n-1}f(x_2)$ for some distinct $x_1, x_2 \in X$. Hence f^n is not an injection and not, in particular, the injection I_X. Now suppose f is not a surjection. There is a $y \in X$ such that $f(x) \neq y$ for all $x \in X$. This implies $f(f^{n-1}(z)) \neq y$ for all $z \in X$. Thus f^n is not a surjection and, in particular, is not the surjection I_X.

A4.15 Let $f \in A^{B \cup C}$ Then $f = f' \cup f''$ where $f' = f \cap (B \times A)$ and $f'' = f \cap C \times A$. $f' \cap f'' = \emptyset$ because $B \cap C = \emptyset$. Now f': $B \to A$ and f'': $C \to A$. Define Φ: $A^{B \cup C} \rightarrowtail\!\!\twoheadrightarrow A^B \times A^C$ as follows: $\Phi(f) = \Phi(f' \cup f'') = (f', f'')$. It can be verified without difficulty that Φ is a function, an injection, and a surjection.

A4.16 Let $f \in A^{B \times C}$. Define Φ: $A^{B \times C} \rightarrowtail\!\!\twoheadrightarrow (A^B)^C$ as follows: $\Phi(f) = \{(c, g) | (c, g) \in C \times A^B$ and $g(b) = f(b, c)\}$. That Φ is injective as argued, thus: $\Phi(f_1) = \Phi(f_2)$. $\{(c, g)|(c, g) \in C \times A^B$ $g(b) = f_1(b, c)\} = \{(c, g)|(c, g) \in C \times A^B$ and $g(b) = f_2(b, c)\}$. $f_1(b, c) = f_2(b, c)$ for all $b \in B$ and $c \in C$. $f_1 = f_2$.

For the surjective property, let $h \in (A^B)^C$. $h(c)$: $B \to A$. $h(c)(b) \in A$. Let f: $B \times C \to A$ such that $f(b, c) = h(c)(b)$. Then

$$\begin{aligned}\Phi(f) &= \{(c, g)|(c, g) \in C \times A^B \text{ and } g(b) = f(b, c)\}\\ &= \{(c, g)|(c, g) \in C \times A^B \text{ and } g(b) = h(c)(b)\}\\ &= \{(c, g)|(c, g) \in C \times A^B \text{ and } g = h(c)\} = h.\end{aligned}$$

A4.17 Define Φ: $A^C \times B^C \rightarrowtail\!\!\twoheadrightarrow (A \times B)^C$ such that $(\phi(f, g))(x) = (f(x), g(x))$ for all $x \in C$. To prove the map injective let $\Phi(f_1, g_1) = \Phi(f_2, g_2)$. $\Phi(f_1, g_1)(x) = \Phi(f_2, g_2)(x)$ for all $x \in C$. $(f_1(x), g_1(x)) = (f_2(x), g_2(x))$ for all $x \in C$. $f_1(x) = f_2(x)$ and $g_1(x) = g_2(x)$ for all $x \in C$. $f_1 = f_2$ and $g_1 = g_2$. $(f_1, g_1) = (f_2, g_2)$. To prove the map surjective, let $h \in (A \times B)^C$. $h(x) \in A \times B$. Let $(h_1(x), h_2(x)) = h(x)$. $h_1 \in A^C$ and $h_2 \in B^C$. $(h_1, h_2) \in A^C \times B^C$. $\Phi(h_1, h_2) = h$ since $\Phi(h_1, h_2)(x) = (h_1(x) h_2(x)) = h(x)$ for all $x \in C$.

A4.18 Verify that Φ: $\Omega \rightarrowtail\!\!\twoheadrightarrow \overline{\Omega}$ such that $\Phi(S) = S \cup I_X$ is a bijection.

A4.19 $\mathcal{E} = \{S|S \in \mathcal{P}(X \times X)$ and S is an equivalence relation on $X\}$. $\mathcal{F} = \{P|P \in \mathcal{P}\mathcal{P}X$ and P is a partition of $X\}$. The proof of the theorem is given on pp. 28, 29 of NST without specifically mentioning functions. Here is the proof with all the notation of functions. Define Φ: $\mathcal{E} \rightarrowtail\!\!\twoheadrightarrow \mathcal{F}$ such that $\Phi(S) = X/S$. To prove Φ injective, let $\Phi(S) = \Phi(T)$. $X/S = X/T$. Let $(x, y) \in S$. $y/S = y/T$. $(x, y) \in T$. $S \subset T$. Likewise $T \subset S$. $S = T$. To prove Φ is a surjection, let $P \in \mathcal{F}$. Define

$$S = \bigcup_{A \in P} A \times A.$$

One must then verify that S is reflexive, symmetric, and transitive, that is, belongs to $\mathcal{E}$. Then one verifies that $\Phi(S) = P$.

A4.20 $P \dagger Q = \{A \cap B \mid A \in P \text{ and } B \in Q\} - \{\emptyset\}$. We prove first that $P \dagger Q$ is a partition of X. Let $A \cap B \in P \dagger Q$. $A \in P$ and $B \in Q$. $A \subset X$ and $B \subset X$. $A \cap B \subset X$. Therefore $P \dagger Q \subset \mathcal{P} X$. Now let $x \in X$. Then $x \in \bigcup P$ and $x \in \bigcup Q$. $x \in A$ for some $A \in P$ and $x \in B$ for some $B \in Q$. $x \in A \cap B$ for some $A \in P$ and $B \in Q$. $x \in \bigcup (P \dagger Q)$. $X \subset \bigcup (P \dagger Q)$. Now suppose $(A \cap B) \cap (C \cap D) \neq \emptyset$. Then there exists an a such that $a \in (A \cap B) \cap (C \cap D)$. $a \in A$ and $a \in C$ imply $A \cap C \neq \emptyset$. Therefore $A = C$. Likewise $B = D$. Hence $A \cap B = C \cap D$. Finally $\emptyset \notin P \dagger Q$ and therefore $P \dagger Q$ is a partition of X.

To prove that $P \dagger Q$ is finer than P and Q let $A \cap B \in P \dagger Q$. Then $A \in P$ and $A \cap B \subset A$; $B \in Q$ and $A \cap B \subset B$. To prove $P \dagger Q$ least fine, let N be any partition finer than both P and Q. $C \in N$ implies $C \subset A$ for some $A \in P$, $C \subset B$ for some $B \in Q$. $C \subset A \cap B$ with $A \cap B \in P \dagger Q$. Thus N is finer than $P \dagger Q$. $P \dagger Q = \sup\{P, Q\}$.

Let $P = \{y/R \mid y \in X\}$ and $Q = \{y/S \mid y \in X\}$. Then $P \dagger Q = \{y/R \cap z/S \mid y \in X,\ z \in X\} - \{\emptyset\} = \{y/R \cap y/S \mid y \in X\} - \{\emptyset\}$ since $z/S \cap y/S = \emptyset$ or $z/S = y/S$. $x \in y/R \cap y/S$ iff $x \in y/R$ and $x \in y/S$ iff $(x, y) \in R$ and $(x, y) \in S$ iff $(x, y) \in R \cap S$ iff $x \in y/(R \cap S)$. Thus $P \dagger Q$ corresponds to $R \cap S$.

Let $\mathcal{Q} = \{U \mid R \subset U \text{ and } S \subset U \text{ and } U \text{ is an equivalence relation on } X\}$. $X \times X \in \mathcal{Q}$ implies $\mathcal{Q} \neq \emptyset$. $T = \bigcap \mathcal{Q}$ is an equivalence relation on X and is $\sup\{R, S\}$. Corresponding to this equivalence relation is a partition N. P and Q are both finer than N. Let $A \in P$. Then $A = y/R$. $x \in y/R$ implies $(x, y) \in R$ which implies $(x, y) \in T$ which implies $x \in y/T$. $y/R \subset y/T$. $y/T = C$ for some $C \in N$. Likewise for Q. Hence N is a lower bound for P and Q. Now suppose P and Q are both finer than M. Then $R \subset U$ and $S \subset U$ where U is the equivalence relation associated with M. Let $C \in N$. Then $C = y/T$ for some $y \in X$. $T \subset U$ because $u \in \mathcal{Q}$. $y/T \subset y/U$. N is finer than M. $N = \inf\{P, Q\}$.

A4.21 That S is an equivalence relation follows from the three properties of equality of sets. Define $\Phi\colon X^X/S \rightarrowtail\twoheadrightarrow \mathcal{P}X-1$ such that $\Phi(f/S) = \text{image } f$. $f/S = g/S$ iff image f = image g iff $\Phi(f/S) = \Phi(g/S)$. Hence Φ is a function and injective. Now let $A \in \mathcal{P}X-1$. Then $A \subset X$ and $A \neq \emptyset$. Let $a \in A$. Define f: $X \to A$ as follows: $f(x) = x$ for $x \in A$ and $f(x) = a$ for $x \notin A$. Then $\Phi(f/S) = \text{image } f = A$. Hence Φ is surjective.

The following observation that $\emptyset \notin$ image Φ is instructive. If image $f = \phi$ for some $f \in X^X$, then $f = \emptyset$. But $\emptyset \notin X^X$.

A4.22 $(f, f) \in S$ because $f(x) - f(x) = 0 \geq 0$ for all $x \in [0, 1]$. $(f, g) \in S$ and $(g, f) \in S$ imply $f = g$ because if $f(x) - g(x) \geq 0$ for all $x \in [0, 1]$ and $g(x) - f(x) \geq 0$ for all $x \in [0, 1]$, then $f(x) - g(x) = 0$ for all $x \in [0, 1]$. Transitivity is also easily verified. The order is not total. For example, $f(x) = x$ and $g(x) = -x + 1$ are noncomparable because $f(0) - g(0) = -1$, $g(1) - f(1) = -1$.

A4.23 That Φ is a function from X to 2^X is clear. That Φ is injective is proven as follows: Suppose $\Phi(A) = \Phi(B)$. $\chi_A = \chi_B$. $\chi_A(x) = \chi_B(x)$ for all $x \in X$. $y \in A$ iff $\chi_A(y) = 1$ iff $\chi_B(y) = 1$ iff $y \in B$. $A = B$. To show that Φ is surjective, let $f \in 2^X$. Define $A = \{x \mid x \in X \text{ and } f(x) = 1\}$. $A \in \mathcal{P}X$ and $\Phi(A) = f$.

A4.24 $\{(0, 1), (1, 1), (2, 0)\}$.

A4.25 $(f \circ i)(x) = f(i(x)) = f(x) = g(x) = g(i(x)) = (g \circ i)(x)$ for all $x \in A$. Let $x \in B$. Then $f(j(x)) = g(j(x))$. $f(x) = g(x)$. $x \in A$ since $x \in X$ and $f(x) = g(x)$. $B \subset A$.

A4.26 Let $\Sigma = \{S \mid S \in \mathcal{P}(X \times Y)$ and S is an equivalence relation on Y such that $\phi_S \circ f = \phi_S \circ g\}$. By ϕ_S is meant the quotient map associated with the equivalence relation S. $\phi_S \circ f = \phi_S \circ g$ iff $\phi_S \circ f(x) = \phi_S \circ g(x)$ for all $x \in X$ iff $f(x)/S = g(x)/S$ for all $x \in X$ iff $(f(x), g(x)) \in S$ for all $x \in X$. $Y \times Y \in \Sigma$ because $Y \times Y$ is an equivalence relation on Y and certainly

$(f(x), g(x)) \in Y \times Y$ for all $x \in X$. Therefore $\Sigma \neq \emptyset$. $R = \bigcap\Sigma$ is an equivalence relation on Y. Cf. 3.13. To show that $\phi_R \circ f = \phi_R \circ g$ one must show that $(f(x), g(x)) \in R$. But $(f(x), g(x)) \in S$ for all $S \in \Sigma$. Therefore $(f(x), g(x)) \in \bigcap\Sigma = R$ for all $x \in X$. Since $R = \bigcap\Sigma$, $R \subset T$ for all $T \in \Sigma$. Define t: $Y/R \twoheadrightarrow Y/T$ such that $t(y/R) = y/T$. That t is a function is clear except perhaps for this property: $y/R = z/R$ implies $(y, z) \in R$ which implies $(y, z) \in T$ which implies $y/T = z/T$. $t(y/R) = t(z/R)$. That t is a surjection: if $y/T \in Y/T$ then $t(y/R) = y/T$.

A4.27 The proof resembles that in 4.14.

A4.28 By 4.27 f is an injection and g is a surjection and also g is an injection and f is a surjection. Hence they are both bijections. Now let $(x, y) \in f$. $(x, x) \in I_X$ implies $(x, z) \in f$ and $(z, x) \in g$ for some $z \in Y$. $(x, z) \in f$ and $(x, y) \in f$ implies $z = y$. Therefore $(y, x) \in g$. Let $(y, x) \in g$. $(y, y) \in I_Y$ implies $(y, w) \in g$ and $(w, y) \in f$ for some $w \in X$. $(y, w) \in g$ and $(y, x) \in g$ imply $x = w$. Hence $(x, y) \in f$. $(x, y) \in f$ iff $(y, x) \in g$. $g = f^{-1}$.

A4.29 Suppose h is not an injection. Then $h(x_1) = h(x_2)$ for some x_1, $x_2 \in X$, $x_1 \neq x_2$. Let g, f be functions defined as follows: g: $X \to X$ such that $g(x) = x_1$ for all $x \in X$ and f: $X \to X$ such that $f(x) = x_2$ for all $x \in X$. $f, g \in X^X$. $f \neq g$. $h \circ f = h \circ g$.

Suppose $h \circ f = h \circ g$ and $f \neq g$. If $f \neq g$ then $f(x_1) \neq g(x_1)$ for some $x_1 \in X$. $h(f(x_1)) = h(g(x_1))$ with $f(x_1) \neq g(x_1)$ means h is not an injection.

A4.30 Suppose h is not a surjection. There exists an $x_1 \in X$ such that $h(x) \neq x_1$ for all $x \in X$. Since $h \in X^X$ never takes the value x_1, we may conclude $X \neq \{x_1\}$. Furthermore, the theorem is true if $X = \emptyset$. Therefore let $x_2 \in X$ with $x_2 \neq x_1$. Define functions $f, g \in X^X$ as follows: f: $X \to X$ such that $f(x) = x_2$

for all $x \in X$, $x \neq x_1$, $f(x_1) = x_1$; g: $X \to X$ such that $g(x) = x_2$ for all $x \in X$. Then $f \neq g$ and $f(h(x)) = g(h(x))$ for all $x \in X$.

Suppose for the converse that $g \circ h = g \circ h$ and $f \neq g$. Then there exists an $x_1 \in X$ such that $f(x_1) \neq g(x_2)$. Hence $h(x)$ never takes the value x_1, for otherwise $h(f(x_1)) \neq h(g(x_1))$. Thus h is not surjective.

A4.31 Functional composition is relational composition which was proved associative in Exercise 3.4. The operation on X^X is the set $\{((f, g), h) | ((f, g), h) \in (X^X \times X^X) \times X^X$ and $h = g \circ f\}$. That the composition of two functions is a function may be verified. I_X is, of course, the neutral element.

A4.32 It needs to be proven that the composition of two injections is an injection. $g(f(x_2)) = g(f(x_1))$ implies $h(x_2) = f(x_1)$ by the injectivity of g and $f(x_2) = f(x_1)$ implies $x_1 = x_2$ by the injectivity of f.

A4.33. The composition of two surjections is a surjection. $y \in X$ implies $f(z) = y$ for some $z \in X$. $f(z) \in X$ implies $g(x) = z$ for some $x \in X$. Hence there exists an $x \in X$ such that $f(g(x)) = y$. $f \circ g$ is surjective.

A4.34 The composition of two bijections is a bijection. If f is a bijection, then f^{-1} is a bijection. $f \circ f^{-1} = f^{-1} \circ f = I_X$.

A4.35 By 3.10, f is reflexive iff $I_X \subset f$. By 4.13, $I_X \subset f$ iff $I_X = f$.

A4.36 f is transitive iff $f \circ f \subset f$ by 3.10. $f \circ f \subset f$ iff $f \circ f = f$ is proven as follows. Certainly $f \circ f = f$ implies $f \circ f \subset f$. For the converse, assume $(x, y) \in f$. $y \in X$ implies $(y, z) \in f$ for some $z \in X$. Hence $(x, z) \in f \circ f$. $(x, z) \in f$. $(x, y) \in f$ and $(x, z) \in f$ imply $y = z$. Therefore $(x, y) \in f \circ f$.

A4.37 f is symmetric iff $f = f^{-1}$ by 3.10 $f = f^{-1}$ iff $f \circ f = I_X$.

A5.1 $(X_i)_{i \in I} = \{(0, X_0), (1, X_1), (2, X_2)\} =$
$= \{(0, \{a, b\}), (1, \{A\}), (2, \{\alpha, \beta, \gamma\})\}$.

$\underset{i \in I}{\times} X_i = \{\{(0, a), (1, A), (2, \alpha)\}, \{(0, a), (1, A), (2, \beta)\},$
$\{(0, a), (1, A), (2, \gamma)\}, \{(0, b), (1, A), (2, \alpha)\},$
$\{(0, b), (1, A), (2, \beta)\}, \{(0, b), (1, A), (2, \gamma)\}\}$.

A5.2 $(X_i)_{i \in I} = I_3$; $\underset{i \in I}{\times} X_i = \emptyset$.

A5.3 $(X_i)_{i \in I} = \{(0, 1), (1, 2), (2, 3)\}$.

$\underset{i \in I}{\times} X_i = \{\{(0,0), (1,0), (2,0)\}, \{(0,0), (1,0), (2,1)\},$
$\{(0,0), (1,0), (2,2)\}, \{(0,0), (1,1), (2,0)\},$
$\{(0,0), (1,1), (2,1)\}, \{(0,0), (1,1), (2,2)\}\}$.

A5.4 Define $f\colon A_0 \times A_1 >\!\!-\!\!\!>\!\!> \underset{i \in 2}{\times} A_i$ such that $f(a_0, a_1) = \{(0, a_0), (1, a_1)\}$. Prove that f is a bijection.

A5.5 Let $c \in A_2 \neq \emptyset$. Define $f\colon A_0 \times A_1 >\!\!-\!\!> \underset{i \in 3}{\times} A_i$ such that $f(a_0, a_1) = \{(0, a_0), (1, a_1), (2, c)\}$. Prove that f is a bijection. If $A_2 = \emptyset$ then $\underset{i \in 3}{\times} A_i = \emptyset$. In this case there exists a bijection iff either A_1 or A_2 is the empty set.

A5.6 Define $f\colon A \times \underset{i \in I}{\times} A_i >\!\!-\!\!> \underset{i \in I}{\times} (A \times A_i)$ such that $f(a, (a_i)_{i \in I}) = ((a, a_i))_{i \in I}$.

The argument that f is an injection goes as follows: Let $f(a, (a_i)_{i \in I}) = f(b, (b_i)_{i \in I})$. $((a, a_i))_{i \in I} = ((b, b_i))_{i \in I}$. $(a, a_i) = (b, b_i)$ for all $i \in I$. $a = b$ and $a_i = b_i$ for all $i \in I$. $a = b$ and $(a_i)_{i \in I} = (b_i)_{i \in I}$. $(a, (a_i)_{i \in I}) = (b, (b_i)_{i \in I})$ and f is injective.

In case $A = I = 2$ and $A_0 = A_1 = 1$ there is no bijection.

A5.7 Define $f\colon \underset{j \in J}{\times} (\underset{i \in I_j}{\times} A_i) >\!\!-\!\!>\!\!> \underset{i \in I}{\times} A_i$ such that $f(((a_i)_{i \in I_j})_{j \in J}) = (a_i)_{i \in I}$. To each member of $\underset{i \in J}{\times} (\underset{i \in I_j}{\times} A_i)$ corresponds a member of $\underset{i \in I}{\times} A_i$ and vice versa.

$((a_i)_{i\in I_j})_{j\in J} = ((b_i)_{i\in I_j})_{j\in J}$ iff $(a_i)_{i\in I_j} = (b_i)_{i\in I_j}$ for all $j \in J$ iff $a_i = b_i$ for all $i \in I_j$ and for all $j \in J$ iff $a_i = b_i$ for all $i \in I$ iff $(a_i)_{i\in I} = (b_i)_{i\in I}$. f is a bijection.

A5.8 Define $\Phi\colon (\underset{i\in I}{\mathsf{X}} A_i)^C \rightarrowtail\!\!\twoheadrightarrow \underset{i\in I}{\mathsf{X}} A_i{}^C$ such that $\Phi(f) = g$ where $g(i)(c) = f(c)(i)$ for all $i \in I$ and all $c \in C$. The motivation for this map can be followed in these lines: $f \in (\underset{i\in I}{\mathsf{X}} A_i)^C$ iff $f(c) \in \underset{i\in I}{\mathsf{X}} A_i$ iff $f(c)(i) \in A_i$ iff $(f(c)(i))_{c\in C} \in A_i{}^C$ iff $((f(c)(i))_{c\in C})_{i\in I} \in \underset{i\in I}{\mathsf{X}} A_i{}^C$.

A5.9 $(x, y) \in (\bigcup_{i\in I} X_i) \times (\bigcup_{j\in J} Y_j)$ iff $x \in \bigcup_{i\in I} X_i$ and $y \in \bigcup_{j\in J} Y_j$ iff $x \in X_i$ for some $i \in I$ and $y \in Y_j$ for some $j \in J$ iff $x \in X_j$ and $y \in Y_j$ for some $(i, j) \in I \times J$ iff $(x, y) \in X_i \times Y_j$ for some $(i, j) \in I \times J$ iff $(x, y) \in \bigcup_{(i,j)\in I\times J} X_i \times Y_j$.

A5.10 $R^{[0,1)}$; $\underset{i\in[0,1]}{\mathsf{X}} R$ or $\underset{i\in[0,1]}{\mathsf{X}} X_i$, $X_i = R$.

A5.11 $\underset{i\in I}{\mathsf{X}} X_i = \underset{A\in\mathcal{P}X-1}{\mathsf{X}} A$. $f \in \underset{A\in\mathcal{P}X-1}{\mathsf{X}} A$ iff $f\colon \mathcal{P}X-1 \to X$ such that $f(A) \in A$. That f assigns to every nonempty subset of X some member of that subset has given f the name "choice function."

A5.12 Define $\Phi\colon R^R \rightarrowtail\!\!\twoheadrightarrow \underset{i\in\omega}{\mathsf{X}} R^{[i,\,i+1)}$ such that $\Phi(f) = (f \cap [i, i+1))_{i\in\omega}$. $\Phi(f) = \Phi(g)$ iff $(f \cap [i, i+1))_{i\in\omega} = (g \cap [i, i+1))_{i\in\omega}$ iff $f \cap [i, i+1) = g \cap [i, i+1)$ for all $i \in \omega$ iff $f = g$. Thus Φ is an injection. To prove Φ surjective, let $g \in \underset{i\in\omega}{\mathsf{X}} R^{[i,\,i+1)}$. Then $\Phi(\bigcup_{i\in\omega} g(i)) = ((\bigcup_{i\in\omega} g(i)) \cap [i, i+1))_{i\in\omega} = (g(i))_{i\in\omega} = g$.

A5.13 The first is the projection of a plane in three space onto the $X_0 - X_1$ plane. If $c = 0$ the projection is a line in the $X_0 - X_1$ plane. If $c \neq 0$, the projection is the entire $X_0 - X_1$ plane.

In the second example the unit sphere is projected onto a closed unit disc.

A6.1 Let f be injective. Let $A \in \mathcal{P}X$. Then let $B = \overline{f}(A)$. We then have $\overline{f}^{-1}(B) = \overline{f}^{-1}(\overline{f}(A)) = A$ (cf. p. 39 of NST) proving $\overline{f}^{-1}$ is surjective.

Now assume f is not an injection. Then $f(x_1) = f(x_2)$ for two distinct elements x_1 and x_2 of X. $\overline{f}^{-1}$ is then not surjective since $\{x_1\} \neq \overline{f}^{-1}(B)$ for any $B \in \mathcal{P}Y$. If $x \in \overline{f}^{-1}(B)$ then $\{x_1, x_2\} \subset \overline{f}^{-1}(B)$ and $\overline{f}^{-1}(B) \neq \{x_1\}$. On the other hand, if $x_1 \notin \overline{f}^{-1}(B)$, then clearly $\overline{f}^{-1}(B) \neq \{x_1\}$.

A6.2 Let f be surjective and assume $\overline{f}^{-1}(B_1) = \overline{f}^{-1}(B_2)$. Let $y_1 \in B_1$. Then since f is surjective $y_1 = f(x)$ for some $x \in X$. $x \in \overline{f}^{-1}(B_1) = \overline{f}^{-1}(B_2)$. $f(x) = y_2$ for some $y_2 \in B_2$. $y_1 = y_2$ since function values are unique yielding $y_1 \in B_2$. $B_1 \subset B_2$. By a symmetrical argument we have $B_2 \subset B_1$. $B_1 = B_2$. $\overline{f}^{-1}$ is injective.

If f is not surjective, there exists a $y_1 \in Y$ such that $y_1 \notin f(X)$. Thus $\overline{f}^{-1}(\emptyset) = \overline{f}^{-1}(\{y_1\})$ and $\overline{f}^{-1}$ is not injective.

A6.3 Let f be injective and let $y \in$ image f. $x \in \overline{f}^{-1}(\{y\})$ iff $f(x) = y$. Since $y \in$ image f there is at least one $x \in \overline{f}^{-1}(\{y\})$. Since f is injective there can be, at most, one x such that $f(x) = y$. Therefore $\overline{f}^{-1}(\{y\})$ is a singleton.

If f is not injective there are an x_1 and an x_2 (distinct) such that $f(x_1) = f(x_2) = y$, say. $\{x_1, x_2\} \subset \overline{f}^{-1}(\{y\})$, which is therefore not a singleton.

A6.4 If f is surjective and B is a nonempty subset of Y, let $y \in B$. $y = f(x)$ for some $x \in X$. $x \in \overline{f}^{-1}(B)$. $\overline{f}^{-1}(B) \neq \emptyset$.

On the other hand, let the inverse image under f of each nonempty subset of Y be a nonempty subset of X. Let $y \in Y$. Then $\{y\}$ is a nonempty subset of Y. $\overline{f}^{-1}(\{y\}) \neq \emptyset$. $f(x) = y$ for some $x \in X$. f is surjective.

A6.5 The missing hypothesis: f is injective.

A6.6 Yes. $x \in \overline{f}^{-1}(B_1 - B_2)$ iff there is a $y \in B_1$ not in B_2 such that $y = f(x)$ iff $x \in \overline{f}^{-1}(B_1)$ and $x \notin \overline{f}^{-1}(B_2)$ iff $x \in \overline{f}^{-1}(B_1) - \overline{f}^{-1}(B_2)$.

A6.7 Yes for the first inclusion. Let $y \in \overline{f}(A_1) - \overline{f}(A_2)$. Then $y = f(x_1)$ for some $x_1 \in A_1$ and $y \neq f(x)$ for any $x \in A_2$. This implies $y = f(x_1)$ for $x_1 \in A_1 - A_2$ which implies $y \in \overline{f}(A_1 - A_2)$. Thus $\overline{f}(A_1) - \overline{f}(A_2) \subset \overline{f}(A_1 - A_2)$. No for the second inclusion. Let f be noninjective. Let $y = f(x_1) = f(x_2)$ with x_1 and x_2 distinct. Then let $A_1 = \{x_1, x_2\}$ and $A_2 = \{x_2\}$. This gives a counterexample.

A6.8 If $y \in \overline{f}(\bigcap_{i \in I} A_i)$ then there is an x such that $y = f(x)$ and $x \in A_i$ for all $i \in I$. This implies $x \in \overline{f}(A_i)$ for all $i \in I$, which in turn implies $x \in \bigcap_{i \in I} \overline{f}(A_i)$. For the counterexample let $I = 2$, $A_0 = \{0, 1\}$, $A_1 = \{0, 2\}$, $f = \{(0, 0), (1, 1), (2, 1)\}$.

A6.9 a) $\mathbf{R} \times \mathbf{R}$. b) Any set including the nonnegative reals. c) The nonnegative reals. d) Not injective since $f(0, 1) = f(1, 0)$ but surjective if range f = image f. e) The closed unit disc centered at $(0, 0)$. f) $[1, \infty)$.

A7.1 Define a relation R on X: $(x_1, x_2) \in R$ iff $f(x_1) = f(x_2)$. Verify that R is an equivalence relation. Associated with the equivalence relation R is a partition X/R and a surjection $\phi: X \twoheadrightarrow X/R$ (the quotient map) such that $\phi(x) = x/R$. Cf. 4.0, 4.19 (pp. 28, 32 of NST). Define $f_1: X/R \to Y$ such that $f_1(x/R) = f(x)$. Now we make several verifications to establish the theorem. a) f_1 is well defined: Let $x_1/R = x_2/R$. Then $f_1(x_1/R) = f(x_1) = f(x_2) = f_1(x_2/R)$ with the inner equality following from the equivalence of x_1 and x_2. b) f_1 is an injection: Let $f_1(x_1/R) = f_1(x_2/R)$. Then $f(x_1) = f(x_2)$. $(x_1, x_2) \in R$. $x_1/R = x_2/R$. c) $f_1 \circ \phi = f$: $(f_1 \circ \phi)(x) = f_1(\phi(x)) = f_1(x/R) = f(x)$.

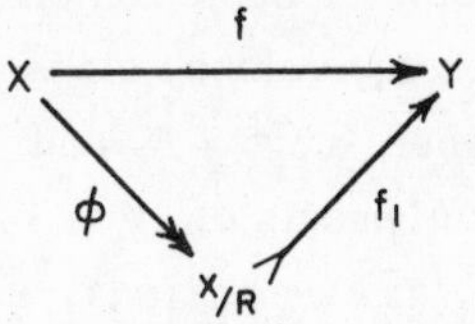

A7.2 Cf. 3.0 and 3.27. Preimage $w = \{(x, y) | (x, y) \in \bigcup\bigcup w$ and $((x, y), z) \in w$ for some $z\} = G \times G$ because a relation which is a function has preimage w = domain w (refer to the definition of a function). $G \times G$ is itself a relation from G to G with preimage $G \times G = G = \{x | x \in \bigcup\bigcup(G \times G)$ and $(x, y) \in G \times G$ for some $y\}$. Hence preimage (preimage w) $= \{x | x \in \bigcup\bigcup\bigcup\bigcup w$ and $((x, y), z) \in w$ for some $y, z\}$.

A7.3 Since $w_i(x_i, y_i) \in G_i$ we have $(w_i(x_i, y_i))_{i \in I} \in \underset{i \in I}{\mathsf{X}} G_i$ and w is well defined. That w is associative is shown as follows:

$$\begin{aligned} w(x, w(y, z)) &= w((x_i)_{i \in I}, w((y_i)_{i \in I}, (z_i)_{i \in I})) \\ &= w((x_i)_{i \in I}, (w_i(y_i, z_i))_{i \in I}) = (w_i(x_i, w_i(y_i, z_i)))_{i \in I} \\ &= w((w_i(x_i, y_i))_{i \in I}, (z_i)_{i \in I}) \\ &= w(w((x_i)_{i \in I}, (y_i)_{i \in I}), (z_i)_{i \in I}) \\ &= w(w(x, y), z). \end{aligned}$$

$e = (e_i)_{i \in I}$ is the identity element. $w(x, e) = w((x_i)_{i \in I}, (e_i)_{i \in I})$

$$= (w_i(x_i, e_i))_{i \in I} = (x_i)_{i \in I} = x .$$

$w(e, x) = x$ also. $w(x, x^{-1}) = w((x_i)_{i \in I}, (x_i^{-1})_{i \in I}) = (w(x, x_i^{-1}))_{i \in I} = (e_i)_{i \in I} = e$. $w(x^{-1}, x) = e$ also.

A7.4 N is a normal subgroup of a group G iff N is a subgroup of $(G, \cdot)$ and $x^{-1}Nx = N$ for all $x \in G$. $(x, y) \in S$ iff $xy^{-1} \in N$. That S is an equivalence relation is verified as follows. $xx^{-1} = e \in N$. Let $xy^{-1} \in N$. $(xy^{-1})^{-1} \in N$. $(y^{-1})^{-1}x^{-1} \in N$. $yx^{-1} \in N$. Now let $xy^{-1} \in N$ and $yz^{-1} \in N$. $xy^{-1}yz^{-1} \in N$. $xez^{-1} \in N$. $xz^{-1} \in N$.

To prove that the defined operation on G/S is independent of the representative of the equivalence class chosen, let $x_1/S = x/S$ and $y_1/S = y/S$. Thus $xx_1^{-1} \in N$, and $yy_1^{-1} \in N$. Using lower case n as notation for elements of N, $x = n_1x_1$ and $y = n_2y_1$. $xy(x_1y_1)^{-1} = n_1x_1n_2y_1y_1^{-1}x_1^{-1} = n_1x_1n_2x_1^{-1} = n_1n_3 \in N$. Hence $x_1y_1/S = xy/S$.

The operation on G/S is associative. $x/S(y/S\ z/S) = x/S\ yz/S = x(yz)/S = (xy)z/S = xy/S\ z/S = (x/S\ y/S)z/S$. $e/S\ x/S = ex/S = x/S$. $x/S\ e/S = xe/S = x/S$. $x/S\ x^{-1}/S = xx^{-1}/S = e/S$. $x^{-1}/S\ x/S = x^{-1}x/S = e/S$.

$$\phi(xy) = xy/S = x/S\ y/S = \phi(x)\phi(y)\ .$$

$$e/S = \{x \mid (x, e) \in S\} = \{x \mid xe^{-1} \in N\} = \{x \mid x \in N\} = N.$$

$$\phi(e) = e/S = N.$$

$$\phi(x) = x/S = \{y \mid yx^{-1} \in N\} = \{y \mid y \in xN\} = xN.$$

A7.5 $N = \overline{f}^{-1}(e_Y)$ is a subgroup of X iff $xy^{-1} \in N$ for all $x, y \in N$. Let $x \in N$ and $y \in N$. Then $f(x) = e_Y$. $f(xy^{-1}) = f(x)[f(y)]^{-1} = e_Ye_Y^{-1} = e_Y$. Therefore $xy^{-1} \in N$. Thus N is a subgroup. N is a normal subgroup iff $x^{-1}Nx = N$ for all $x \in X$. Let $n \in N$. Then $f(x^{-1}nx) = f(x^{-1})f(n)f(x) = f(x^{-1})e_Yf(x) = e_Y$ and one has shown that $x^{-1}Nx \subset N$. Let $n \in N$. $n = x^{-1}$ $x^{-1}xnx^{-1}x = x^{-1}n_1x$. Therefore $N \subset x^{-1}Nx$. Thus $N = x^{-1}Nx$ for any $x \in X$.

$(x, y) \in T$ iff $f(x) = f(y)$ iff $f(x)[f(y)]^{-1} = e_Y$ iff
$f(xy^{-1}) = e_Y$ iff $xy^{-1} \in N$.

$$f_1(x/N\ y/N) = f_1(xy/N) = f(xy) = f(x)f(y) = f_1(x/N)f_1(y/N).$$

$[f(x) = f(y)$ implies $x = y]$ iff
$[f(xy^{-1}) = e_Y$ implies $xy^{-1} = e_X]$ iff
$[f(a) = e_Y$ implies $a = e_X]$ iff
$[\text{kernel } f = \{e_X\}]$.

A7.6 First, the defined relation is an equivalence relation on R. $x - x = 0 \in A$. If $x - y \in A$ then $-(x - y) \in A$, which implies

$y-x \in A$. Let $x-y \in A$ and $y-z \in A$. Then $(x-y)+(y-z) \in A$. $x-z \in A$.

Let $x/S = x_1/S$ and $y/S = y_1/S$. Then $x-x_1 \in A$ and $y-y_1 \in A$. $x+y-(x_1+y_1) \in A$ Thus $(x+y)/S = (x_1+y_1)/S$. Addition is well defined. Now letting lower case a represent members of A, we show that multiplication on the partition is well defined. Let $x = x_1+a_1$, $y = y_1+a_2$. $xy = (x_1+a_1)(y_1+a_2) = x_1y_1 + a_1y_1 + a_2x_1 + a_1a_2 = x_1y_1 + a_3$. Hence $xy-x_1y_1 \in A$ and $xy/S = x_1y_1/S$.

The verification of the associative, commutative, and distributive laws is trivial. For example, here is the distributive law: $x/S(y/S+z/S) = x/S\cdot(y+z)/S = x(y+z)/S = (xy+xz)/S = xy/S+xz/S = x/S\ y/S + x/S\ z/S$. $e/S\ x/S = ex/S = x/S$.
$\phi(x+y) = (x+y)/S = x/S + y/S = \phi(x)+\phi(y)$.
$\phi(xy) = xy/S = x/S\ y/S = \phi(x)\phi(y)$.
$x/S = \{y \mid y-x \in A\} = \{y \mid y \in x+A\} = x+A = \phi(x)$.

A7.7 One applies the fundamental mapping theorem and verifies the algebraic properties as in 7.5. Let $A = \overline{f}^{-1}(0_S)$. A is an ideal of R because if $f(x) = 0_S$, $f(y) = 0_S$ and $r \in R$ then $f(x-y) = 0_S$ and $f(rx) = f(r)f(x) = f(r)\,0_S = 0_S$. Letting T be the equivalence relation mentioned in the fundamental mapping theorem, we have $(x, y) \in T$ iff $f(x) = f(y)$ iff $f(x)-f(y) = 0_S$ iff $f(x-y) = 0_S$ iff $x-y \in A$. Hence R/A of 7.6 and R/T of the fundamental mapping theorem are the same.

$$f_1(x/A + y/A) = f_1((x+y)/A) = f(x+y) = f(x)+f(y)$$
$$= f_1(x/A)+f_1(y/A).$$
$$f_1(x/A\ y/A) = f_1(xy/A) = f(xy) = f(x)f(y) = f_1(x/A)f_1(y/A).$$

A7.8 By the fundamental mapping theorem, there exist an equivalence relation S on X, a surjection ϕ: $X \longrightarrow\!\!> X/S$ and an injection f_1: $X/S >\!\!\longrightarrow Y$ such that $f = f_1 \circ \phi$. Let g: $X/S >\!\!\longrightarrow\!\!> f(X)$ such that $g(x/S) = f_1(x/S)$ and ψ: $f(X) >\!\!\longrightarrow Y$ such that $\psi(y) = y$. Then $f_1 = \psi \circ g$ and g is surjective as well as injective. For all $y \in f(X)$ there exists an $x \in X$ such that $y = f(x)$. Therefore $y = f_1(x/S) = g(x/S)$.

A7.9 $p_1: A \times B \longrightarrow\!\!> A$ and $p_2: A \times B \longrightarrow\!\!> B$ are projections. Let the function $\phi: X \longrightarrow A \times B$ be defined as follows: $\phi(x) = (f(x), g(x))$. Then $(p_1 \circ \phi)(x) = p_1(\phi(x)) = p_1(f(x), g(x)) = f(x)$ and $(p_2 \circ \phi)(x) = p_2(\phi(x)) = p_2(f(x), g(x)) = g(x)$.

Now let ψ be any other function from X to $A \times B$ such that $p_1 \circ \psi = f$ and $p_2 \circ \psi = g$. Suppose that $\psi(x) = (y_1, y_2)$. Then $p_1(y_1, y_2) = y_1 = f(x)$ and $p_2(y_1, y_2) = y_2 = g(x)$. Therefore $\phi = \psi$.

A7.10 $A \bar{\cup} B = (A \times \{0\}) \cup (B \times \{1\})$. Define $\phi: A \bar{\cup} B \to X$ such that $\phi(a, 0) = f(a)$ and $\phi(b, 1) = g(b)$. Then $(\phi \circ i_1)(a) = \phi(i_1(a)) = \phi(a, 0) = f(a)$ and $(\phi \circ i_2)(b) = \phi(i_2(b)) = \phi(b, 1) = g(b)$. The verification of the uniqueness is trivial.

A7.11 The operation is associative. $f(gh)(x) = f(x)(gh)(x) = f(x)[g(x)h(x)] = [f(x)g(x)]h(x) = (fg)(x)h(x) = (fg)h(x)$. Let e be the identity of G. Then the constant function (also named e) e: $X \longrightarrow G$ such that $e(x) = e$ for all $x \in X$ is the identity of G^X. $(fe)(x) = f(x)e(x) = f(x)$ and $(ef)(x) = e(x)f(x) = f(x)$. Now given $f: X \longrightarrow G$, let $g: X \longrightarrow G$ be the function with values $g(x) = (f(x))^{-1}$ which is for each x the inverse in G. Then $(fg)(x) = f(x)g(x) = f(x)(f(x))^{-1} = e$. Similarly, $gf = e$ and each member of G^X has an inverse.

If G is commutative, then it is easily verified that G^X is also commutative. Define $\Phi: G \rightarrowtail G^X$ such that $\Phi(a)$ is this member of G^X, $\Phi(a): X \to G$ such that $\Phi(a)(x) = a$ for all $x \in X$. In words, $\Phi(a)$ is the constant function with the value a. Φ is a homomorphism, for $\Phi(ab)(x) = ab = \Phi(a)(x)\Phi(b)(x) = (\Phi(a)\Phi(b))(x)$ for all $x \in X$.

If $X = \emptyset$ then $G^{\emptyset}$ has but one function in it. If G is then not trivial ($\neq \{e\}$), then Φ is not injective. On the other hand, if $X \neq \emptyset$ suppose $\Phi(a) = \Phi(b)$. Then $\Phi(a)(x) = \Phi(b)(x)$

for all $x \epsilon X$. Let x_1 be a member of nonempty X. $\Phi(a)(x_1) = \Phi(b)(x_1)$. $a = b$ yielding Φ injective.

A7.12 The operations for the ring of functions are these obvious ones: $(f+g)(x) = f(x) + g(x)$, $(fg)(x) = f(x)g(x)$ for all $x \epsilon X$. The zero element of the ring is the constant function with the value zero for all $x \epsilon X$. There exist functions in R^X, provided that X has at least two elements, which are zero for some values and non-zero for others. These functions have no multiplicative inverse in R^X. Thus R^X is not, in general, a field even if R is.

A7.13 Assume $x \epsilon A \cap B$. Then $x \epsilon A$ and $x \epsilon B$. $\chi_A(x) = 1$ and $\chi_B(x) = 1$. $\chi_A(x)\chi_B(x) = 1$. $(\chi_A\chi_B)(x) = 1$. Assume $x \notin A \cap B$. Then $x \notin A$ or $x \notin B$. $\chi_A(x) = 0$ or $\chi_B(x) = 0$. $(\chi_A\chi_B)(x) = 0$. Hence we have proven $\chi_{A \cap B} = \chi_A\chi_B$.

If $x \epsilon A'$ then $x \notin A$. $\chi_A(x) = 0$. $1 - \chi_A(x) = 1$. If $x \notin A'$ then $x \epsilon A$. $\chi_A(x) = 1$. $1 - \chi_A(x) = 0$. Thus we have proven $\chi_{A'} = 1 - \chi_A$.

If $x \epsilon A \cup B$ then ($x \epsilon A$ and $x \epsilon B$) or ($x \epsilon A$ and $x \notin B$) or ($x \notin A$ and $x \epsilon B$). ($\chi_A(x) = 1$ and $\chi_B(x) = 1$) or ($\chi_A(x) = 1$ and $\chi_B(x) = 0$) or ($\chi_A(x) = 0$ and $\chi_B(x) = 1$). $\chi_A(x) + \chi_B(x) - \chi_A\chi_B(x) = 1$. On the other hand, if $x \notin A \cup B$ then $x \notin A$ and $x \notin B$. $\chi_A(x) = 0$ and $\chi_B(x) = 0$. $\chi_A(x) + \chi_B(x) - \chi_A(x)\chi_B(x) = 0$. Therefore $\chi_{A \cup B} = \chi_A + \chi_B - \chi_A\chi_B$.

Referring to 4.23, one has only to prove that Φ is a homomorphism. This requires $\chi_{A+B} = \chi_A + \chi_B$ and $\chi_{A \cap B} = \chi_A\chi_B$, which can be verified.

A7.14 $f \epsilon A$ and $g \epsilon A$ implies $f(x) = 0$ and $g(x) = 0$ for all $x \epsilon D'$. $f(x) - g(x) = 0$ for all $x \epsilon D'$. $f - g \epsilon A$. Now assume $f \epsilon R^X$ and $g \epsilon A$. $g(x) = 0$ for all $x \epsilon D'$. $f(x)g(x) = 0$ for all $x \epsilon D'$. $fg \epsilon A$. A is an ideal.

Let R be a field and $D' = \{a\}$. A is then the set of all functions which are zero at a. R^X/A is a ring by 7.6 and A is its zero element. To prove that R^X/A is a field, let f/A be a nonzero element of R^X/A. Then $f \notin A$ and $f(a) \neq 0$. If 1 represents the multiplicative identity of R, then represent the constant function by the same symbol. Let g be the constant function such that $g(x) = (f(a))^{-1}$. $f(a)g(a) - 1 = 0$ in R. Therefore $fg - 1 \in A$ or $fg = 1/A$.

A7.15 K^X is a commutative group and is the set of vectors for the vector space. It is readily verified that these further properties are satisfied: $(km)f = k(mf)$, $(k+m)f = kf + mf$, $k(f+g) = kf + kg$, $1f = f$ for all $k, m \in K$, $f, g \in K^X$.

A7.16 For $(a_{ij}), (b_{ij}) \in K^{I\times J}$ by definition $(a_{ij}) + (b_{ij}) = (a_{ij} + b_{ij})$. $K^{I\times J}$ is a group: $(a_{ij}) + [(b_{ij}) + (c_{ij})] = [(a_{ij}) + (b_{ij})] + (c_{ij})$, $(a_{ij}) = 0$ iff $a_{ij} = 0$ for all $(i, j) \in I \times J$, $-(a_{ij}) = (-a_{ij})$, $(a_{ij}) + (b_{ij}) = (b_{ij}) + (a_{ij})$. And by definition, the scalar multiplication: for $k \in K$, $(a_{ij}) \in K^{I\times J}$, $k(a_{ij}) = (ka_{ij})$. Furthermore, $(k+m)(a_{ij}) = k(a_{ij}) + m(a_{ij})$, $k[(a_{ij}) + (b_{ij})] = k(a_{ij}) + k(b_{ij})$, $k[m(a_{ij})] = (km)(a_{ij})$, $1 \cdot (a_{ij}) = (a_{ij})$.

A7.17 $K^{J\times J}$ is a special case of $K^{I\times J}$ yielding the vector space properties. The remaining necessary properties are proven in this manner:

$$k[(a_{ih})(b_{hj})] = k\left(\sum_{h\in J} a_{ih}b_{hj}\right) = \left(k\sum_{h\in J} a_{ih}b_{hj}\right)$$

$$[k(a_{ih})](b_{hj}) = (ka_{ih})(b_{hj}) = \left(\sum_{h\in J} ka_{ih}b_{hj}\right) = \left(k\sum_{h\in J} a_{ih}b_{hj}\right)$$

$$(a_{ih})[k(b_{hj})] = (a_{ih})(kb_{hj}) = \left(\sum_{h\in J} a_{ih}kb_{hj}\right) = \left(k\sum_{h\in J} a_{ih}b_{hj}\right)$$

Relying upon the associativity and commutativity of the field K, one may prove the product associative:

$$(a_{ih})[(b_{hm})(c_{mj})] = (a_{ih})\left(\sum_{m\in J} b_{hm}c_{mj}\right) = \left(\sum_{h\in J} a_{ih}\sum_{m\in J} b_{hm}c_{mj}\right)$$

$$= \left(\sum_{h\in J}\sum_{m\in J} a_{ih}b_{hm}c_{mj}\right) = \left(\sum_{m\in J}\sum_{h\in J} a_{ih}b_{hm}c_{mj}\right) = \text{etc.}$$

To prove noncommutativity, consider this example: $J = \{1, 2\}$,

$$a_{11} = a_{21} = a_{22} = 0; \quad a_{12} = 1$$
$$b_{11} = b_{12} = b_{22} = 0; \quad b_{21} = 1.$$

$\delta_{ij} = 0$ if $i \neq j$ and $\delta_{ij} = 1$ if $i = j$ has the required property.

A7.18 $(h_b h_a)(x) = h_b(h_a(x)) = h_b(ax) = bax = h_{ba}(x)$. Define Φ: $E >\!\!\longrightarrow\!\!> H$ such that $\Phi(a) = h_a$. $\Phi(ab) = h_{ab} = h_a h_b = \Phi(a)\Phi(b)$. Let $\Phi(a) = \Phi(b)$. $h_a = h_b$. $h_a(x) = h_b(x)$ for all $x \in E$. $ax = bx$ for all $x \in E$. $ae = be$. $a = b$. Finally, the homomorphic image of a group is itself a group.

A7.19 S is the set of Cauchy sequences with rational values. To prove S is a subring of Q^N, let $r, s \in S$. For $\varepsilon/2 > 0$ there exists a positive integer n_1 such that if $i, j \geq n_1$, then $|r(i) - r(j)| < \varepsilon/2$; there exists a positive integer n_2 such that if $i, j \geq n_2$, then $|s(i) - s(j)| < \varepsilon/2$. Then $|(r-s)(i) - (r-s)(j)| = |r(i) - s(i) - r(j) + s(j)| \leq |r(i) - r(j)| + |s(i) - s(j)| < \varepsilon$ for $i, j \geq \max\{n_1, n_2\}$. Therefore $r - s \in S$. We now demonstrate multiplicative closure. Again let $r, s \in S$. There is a positive integer n_1 such that if $i, j \geq n_1$, then $|r(i) - r(j)| < 1$. Moreover, for $i \geq n_1$ one has $|r(i)| - |r(n_1)| \leq |r(i) - r(n_1)| < 1$ or $|r(i)| < 1 + |r(n_1)| = B_1$, say. Likewise, there exists a positive integer n_2 such that if $i \geq n_2$, then $|s(i)| \leq 1 + |s(n_2)| = B_2$. Furthermore, there exists a positive integer n_3 such that if $i, j \geq n_3$, then $|r(i) - r(j)| < \varepsilon/2B_2$, and there exists a positive integer n_4 such that if $i, j \geq n_4$, then $|s(i) - s(j)| < \varepsilon/2B_1$. Now assembling all these inequalities we have:

$$\begin{aligned}
|(rs)(i) - (rs)(j)| &\leq |r(i)s(i) - r(j)s(j)| \\
&\leq |r(i)s(i) - r(i)s(j)| + |r(i)s(j) - r(j)s(j)| \\
&\leq |r(i)|\,|s(i) - s(j)| + |r(i) - r(j)|\,|s(j)| \\
&< B_1 \cdot \varepsilon/2B_1 + B_2 \cdot \varepsilon/2B_2 = \varepsilon
\end{aligned}$$

provided that $i, j \geq \max\{n_1, n_2, n_3, n_4\}$. Therefore $rs \in S$ and S is a subring.

To prove that N is an ideal of S, let $r, s \in N$. For $\varepsilon/2 > 0$ there exists a positive integer n_1 such that if $i \geq n_1$, then $|r(i)| < \varepsilon/2$, and there exists a positive integer n_2 such that if $i \geq n_2$, then $|s(i)| < \varepsilon/2$. Then $|(r-s)(i)| \leq |r(i)-s(i)| \leq |r(i)| + |s(i)| < \varepsilon$ for $i \geq \max\{n_1, n_2\}$. Therefore $r-s \in N$. Now let $r \in S$ and $s \in N$. There exists a positive integer n_1 so that if $i \geq n_1$, then $|r(i)| \leq B_1$, and there exists a positive integer n_2 so that if $i \geq n_2$, then $|s(i)| < \varepsilon/B_1$. Then $|rs(i)| \leq |r(i)||s(i)| < B_1 \cdot \varepsilon/B_1 = \varepsilon$ for $i \geq \max\{n_1, n_2\}$. Therefore $rs \in N$. N is an ideal of the ring S of Cauchy sequences with rational values.

To prove that the quotient ring S/N is a field (cf. 7.6) let $r/N \in S/N$ with $r/N \neq 0/N$ and demonstrate the existence of $s/N \in S/N$ such that $r/N \cdot s/N = 1/N$ where 0 and 1 are the constant sequences with each value equal to the rational numbers 0 and 1, respectively. First there exist a positive integer n and a positive rational C such that $|r(i)| \geq C$ for all $i \geq n$. Assume that this were not the case. Let $\varepsilon > 0$ be given. Then there is a positive integer n such that if $i, j \geq n$ then $|r(i) - r(j)| < \varepsilon/2$. Let $|r(m)| < \varepsilon/2$ with $m \geq n$. Then $|r(i)| \leq |r(i)-r(m)| + |r(m)| < \varepsilon$ for $i \geq n$. Therefore $r \in N$. But this contradicts $r/N \neq 0/N$. Now to continue the search for the reciprocal, define a sequence s as follows: $s(i) = 1/r(i)$ if $r(i) \neq 0$ and $s(i) = 1$ if $r(i) = 0$. There exists a positive integer n_1 such that if $i \geq n_1$, then $|r(i)| \geq C > 0$, and there exist a positive integer n_2 such that if $i, j \geq n_2$, then $|r(i)-r(j)| < \varepsilon C^2$. Then $|s(i) - s(j)| = |1/r(i) - 1/r(j)| = |r(j)-r(i)|/|r(i)r(j)| < \varepsilon C^2/C^2 = \varepsilon$ provided $i, j \geq \max\{n_1, n_2\}$. $s \in S$. $r(i)s(i) = 1$ for all $i \geq n_1$. $r(i)s(i) - 1 = 0$ for all $i \geq n_1$. $rs - 1 \in N$ yielding $rs/N = 1/N$. Thus S/N is a field.

Define $\Phi\colon Q \rightarrowtail S/N$ with $\Phi(q) = \{(n, q) \mid n \in \mathrm{N}\}/N$. In words, the image of the rational number q under the mapping Φ is the equivalence class containing the constant sequence with each alue equal to q. In order to show that Φ is injective, let $\Phi(q) =$ (p). Then $\{(n, q) | n \in \mathrm{N}\}/N = \{(n, p) | n \in \mathrm{N}\}/N$. $\{(n, q) | n \in \mathrm{N}\}$ $\{(n, p) | n \in \mathrm{N}\} \in N$. $\{(n, q-p) | n \in \mathrm{N}\} \in N$. Given $\varepsilon > 0$, ere is a positive integer n_1 such that $|q-p| < \varepsilon$. But this is ly possible provided $q - p = 0$, proving Φ is injective. It is sy to show that Φ is a homomorphism.

7.20 $\varepsilon(\sigma) = (1/D)\sigma(D)$; $\varepsilon(\tau) = (1/D)\tau(D)$. Then $\varepsilon(\tau \circ \sigma) =$ $/D)(\tau \circ \sigma)(D) = (1/D)\tau(\sigma(D)) = (1/D)\tau(D \cdot \varepsilon(\sigma)) =$ $/D)\varepsilon(\sigma)\tau(D) = \varepsilon(\sigma)\varepsilon(\tau)$.

0 is the empty set and it has one bijection, namely, the npty set. $\mathfrak{S}_0 = \{\emptyset\} = 1$. The definition does not cover this ase as far as sign is concerned. However, if ε is to be a homo-orphism, $\varepsilon(\emptyset)$ must be 1. Thus $\mathfrak{A}_0 = 1$ also. $1 = \{0\}$ has xactly one bijection $\{(0,0)\}$ and it is even. Thus $\mathfrak{S}_1 = \mathfrak{A}_1 =$ $(0,0)\}\}$ ($= \{\{\{\{0\}\}\}\}$ curiously).

$$2 = \{0, 1\}. \quad \mathfrak{S}_2 = \{\{(0,0), (1,1)\}, \{(0,1), (1,0)\}\}.$$
$$\mathfrak{A}_2 = \{\{(0,0), (1,1)\}\}.$$
$$3 = \{0, 1, 2\}. \quad \mathfrak{S}_3 = \{\{(0,0), (1,1), (2,2)\}, \{(0,1), (1,0), (2,2)\}, \{(0,0), (1,2), (2,1)\}, \{(0,2), (1,0), (2,1)\}, \{(0,2), (1,1), (2,0)\}, \{(0,1), (1,2), (2,0)\}\}.$$
$$\mathfrak{A}_3 = \{\{(0,0), (1,1), (2,2)\}, \{(0,2), (1,0), (2,1)\}, \{(0,1), (1,2), (2,0)\}\}.$$

8.1 Let P be a set with the property that if $\{x, y\}$ is any un-rdered pair, then $\{x, y\} \in P$. Then $U = \bigcup P$ is a set such that if is any set whatsoever, then $z \in U$. This contradicts Russell's eorem: no set contains every set.

A8.2 $x \in \omega$ implies $x \subset \omega$ is equivalent to $y \in n$ implies $y \in \omega$ for all $n \in \omega$. Let $S = \{n \mid n \in \omega$ and $y \in n$ implies $y \in \omega\}$. $S = \omega$ by an easy induction.

A8.3 There is the following result on p. 49 of NST: If E is a nonempty subset of some natural number, then there exists an element k in E such that $k \in m$ whenever m is an element of E distinct from k. Use this result to prove 8.3. Let $E \subset \omega$, $E \neq \emptyset$ $n \in E$ for some $n \in \omega$. $E \cap n^+$ is then a nonempty subset of n^+. Let $k \in E \cap n^+$ such that $k \in m$ for all $m \in E \cap n^+$, $m \neq k$. Now if $m \notin n^+$ and $m \in E$, then $n^+ = m$ or $n^+ \in m$. Thus if $k \in E \cap n^+$, it is also true that $k \in m$.

A8.4 Using the total ordering of ω, show that impossibility of the other alternatives.

A8.5 Into the lemma "it is not the case that $x \in n$ and $n \subset x$" substitute n for x, getting "it is not the case that $n \in n$ and $n \subset n$." Since $n \subset n$, one has $n \notin n$.

A8.6 Let $S = \{n \mid n \in \omega$ and $(0 \in n$ or $n = 0)\}$. Obviously $0 \in S$. Now suppose that $n \in S$. $n = 0$ or $0 \in n$. If $n = 0$ then $n^+ = 0 \cup \{0\}$ which contains 0. If $0 \in n$ then $n^+ = n \cup \{n\}$ also contains 0. Therefore $S = \omega$. Thus if $n \neq 0$ then $0 \in n$ for all $n \in \omega$.

A8.7 Let E be a finite set and let m be the natural number equivalent to E. Let $S = \{n \mid n \in \omega$ and n is equivalent to some set F such that $E \cup F$ is finite$\}$. $0 \in S$, for if 0 is equivalent to F, then $F = \emptyset$ and $E \cup \emptyset = E$ which is equivalent to m. Suppose $n \in S$. Let F be a set equivalent to n^+. Then there exists a bijection $f: F >\!\!\longrightarrow\!\!> n^+$. Let $a \in F$ such that $(a, n) \in f$. $F - \{a\}$ is equivalent to n by the bijection $f - \{(a, n)\}$. Then by the induction hypothesis $E \cup (F - \{a\})$ is finite and equivalent to some natural number p by some bijection g. If $a \in E$ then $E \cup F$ is equivalent to p because $E \cup (F - \{a\}) = E \cup F$.

f $a \notin E$ then $g \cup \{(a, p)\}$: $E \cup F >\!\!\longrightarrow\!\!> p^+$ and $E \cup F$ is equivalent to the natural number p^+. Therefore $n^+ \in S$. $S = \omega$.

A8.8 Let A be equivalent to 2 and B be equivalent to 1. Suppose that $A \subset B$. Since A is equivalent to 2, there exists a bijection f: $2 >\!\!\longrightarrow\!\!> A$. Since f is a bijection, the numbers of A are exactly $f(0)$ and $f(1)$ with $f(0) \neq f(1)$. Since B is equivalent to 1, there exists a bijection g: $1 >\!\!\longrightarrow\!\!> B$. B has only the member $g(0)$. $A \subset B$ implies $f(0) = g(0)$ and $f(1) = g(0)$ and therefore $f(0) = f(1)$, contradicting f's being a bijection.

A8.9 Let $S = \{n \mid n \in \omega$ and $(A_0 \subsetneqq A_n$ or $n = 0)\}$. Obviously $0 \in S$. Assume $n \in S$. If $n = 0$, then $n^+ = 1$ and $A_0 \subsetneqq A_1$ as given. If $A_0 \subsetneqq A_n$, then $A_0 \subsetneqq A_{n^+}$ since $A_n \subsetneqq A_{n^+}$ is given. Hence $n^+ \in S$.

A8.10 Let $m, n \in \omega$ and assume that $m^+ = n^+$. $m \cup \{m\} = n \cup \{n\}$. From this set equality one may conclude

$$(m \in n \text{ or } m = n) \text{ and } (n \in m \text{ or } n = m).$$

Thus one of the following must be true:

1. $m \in n$ and $n \in m$, 2. $m \in n$ and $n = m$,
3. $n \in m$ and $m = n$, 4. $m = n$ and $n = m$.

Alternatives 2, 3, 4 all immediately yield $m = n$. Suppose alternative 1. $m \in n$ and $n \in m$. By the quoted lemma, $m \subset n$ and $n \subset m$ giving $m = n$. Thus in all cases $m = n$. Using the other lemma, one can actually prove that alternative 1 cannot occur (see NST), but this does not affect the validity of this demonstration.

A8.11 It is sufficient to prove $A_0 = A_i$ for all $i \in \omega$. By an argument like that in A8.9, $A_0 \subset A_i$ for all $i \in \omega$. But

$$A_i \subset \bigcup_{j \in \omega} A_j \subset A_0$$

and therefore $A_0 = A_i$.

A8.12 $x \in \liminf(X\ )_{i \in \omega}$ implies $x \ \bigcap_{i > k} X_i$ for some $k \in \omega$.

There exists a $k \in \omega$ such that $x \in X_i$ for all $i > k$.

$X \in \bigcup_{\substack{i\in\omega \\ i>j}} X_i$ any $j \in \omega$ because if not, $x \notin X_i$ for all $i > j$.

$$x \in \bigcap_{j\in\omega}\Big(\bigcup_{\substack{i\in\omega \\ i>j}} X_i\Big).$$

A8.13 $[0, \infty)$, $\{0\}$; $\limsup = [-1, +1]$, $\liminf = \{0\}$.

A8.14 Let $(X_i)_{i\in\omega}$ be an increasing sequence; $X_i \subset X_{i+1}$ for all $i \in \omega$. Then $\bigcap_{\substack{i\in\omega \\ i>j}} X_i = X_j$.

$$\liminf (X_i)_{i\in\omega} = \bigcup_{j\in\omega} \bigcap_{\substack{j\in\omega \\ i>j}} X_i = \bigcup_{j\in\omega} X_j .$$

$$\limsup (X_i)_{i\in\omega} = \bigcap_{j\in\omega}\Big(\bigcup_{\substack{i>j \\ i\in\omega}} X_i\Big) \subset \bigcup_{i\in\omega} X_i$$

$$= \liminf (X_i)_{i\in\omega} .$$

A similar proof works for the decreasing sequence.

A8.15 a) $X = \omega$, $f\colon \omega \to \omega$ such that $f(x) = x^+$, $a = m$ and $u\colon \omega \to \omega$ such that $u(n) = m + n = s_m(n)$.

b) $X = \omega$, $f\colon \omega \to \omega$ such that $f(x) = x + m = s_x(m)$, $a = 0$, and $u\colon \omega \to \omega$ such that $u(n) = mn = p_m(n)$.

c) $X = \omega$, $f\colon \omega \to \omega$ such that $f(x) = xm = p_x(m)$, $a = 1$, and $u\colon \omega \to \omega$ such that $u(n) = m^n$.

d) X = a set of functions containing all derivatives for each function, $f\colon X \to X$ such that $f(g) = d/dx\, g$, $a = g$, and $u\colon \omega \to X$ such that $u(n) = d^n/dx^n\, g$.

e) X = a set of functions for which composition is defined and which contains the identity function, $f\colon X \to X$ such that $f(x) = x \circ g$, a = the identity function, $u\colon \omega \to X$ such that $u(n) = g^n$.

A8.16 ω is a set. The Cartesian product of a set is a set. Hence $(\omega\times\omega)\times\omega$ is a set. By the axiom of specification, s is a set. $s\colon \omega\times\omega \to \omega$ is a function since $s_x(y)$ is unique. A function from $\omega\times\omega$ to ω is an operation on ω. To prove that s is an associative operation (adopting the standard notation for an operation), it must be proven that $x + (y+z) = (x+y) + z$ for all $x, y, z \epsilon \omega$. Let $S = \{n \mid n \epsilon \omega$ and $x + (y+n) = (x+y) + n$ for all $x, y \epsilon \omega\}$. By definition $y + 0 = y$, $x + y^+ = (x+y)^+$. Thus $x + (y+0) = (x+y) + 0$ implies $0 \epsilon S$. Assume $n \epsilon S$. $x + (y+n^+) = x + (y+n)^+ = (x+(y+n))^+ = ((x+y) + n)^+ = (x+y) + n^+$. Therefore $n^+ \epsilon S$. $S = \omega$. s is associative.

It is true by definition that $x + 0 = x$ for all $x \epsilon \omega$. Now it will be proven that $0 + y = y$ for all $y \epsilon \omega$. Let $S = \{n \mid n \epsilon \omega$ and $0 + n = n\}$. $0 \epsilon S$ since $0 + 0 = 0$. Assume $n \epsilon S$. Then $0 + n^+ = (0+n)^+ = n^+$. $n^+ \epsilon S$. 0 is then the identity element for (+). Furthermore, it has been proven that $0 + x = x + 0$ for all $x \epsilon \omega$. $n^+ = (n+0)^+ = n + 0^+ = n + 1$. Let $S = \{n \mid n \epsilon \omega$ and $1 + n = n^+\}$. $1 + 0 = 1 = 0^+$ yields $0 \epsilon S$. $1 + n^+ = (1+n)^+ = (n^+)^+ = n^+ + 1$. Therefore $n \epsilon S$ implies $n^+ \epsilon S$. Thus $1 + y = y^+$ for all $y \epsilon \omega$. With these preliminaries the commutativity of (+) can be proven. Let $S = \{n \mid n \epsilon \omega$ and $n + y = y + n\}$. $0 \epsilon S$. Assume $n \epsilon S$. Then $(n^+ + y) = (n+1) + y = n + (1+y) = n + (y+1) = (n+y) + 1 = (y+n) + 1 = y + (n+1) = y + n^+$. Therefore $n^+ \epsilon S$. $S = \omega$.

To prove cancellation, let $S = \{n \mid n \epsilon \omega$ and $x + n = y+n$ implies $x = y\}$. $0 \epsilon S$ because $x + 0 = y + 0$ implies $x = y$. Assume $n \epsilon S$. $x + n^+ = y + n^+$ implies $(x+n)^+ = (y+n)^+$, which implies $x + n = y + n$, which in turn implies $x = y$. $n^+ \epsilon S$. $S = \omega$.

A8.17 Similar to 8.16.

A8.20 Assume X is not infinite. Then there exists an $n \epsilon \omega$ and a bijection f: $X >\!\!\longrightarrow\!\!> n$. Assume X is Dedekind infinite. Then there exists a proper subset A of X and a bijection g: $X >\!\!\longrightarrow\!\!> A$. The restriction of f to the domain A maps A onto a proper subset of n. $(f|A)$: $A >\!\!\longrightarrow\!\!> a$. $(f|A) \circ g \circ f^{-1}$ is then a bijection of n onto a, a proper subset of n. This is impossible (cf. p.52 of NST). Thus X is not Dedekind infinite.

Assume now that X is infinite. Then there exists a u: $\omega >\!\!\longrightarrow X$ (cf. p. 61 of NST). Let s represent the successor function. s: $\omega >\!\!\longrightarrow\!\!> \omega - \{0\}$ such that $s(n) = n + 1$. Let $v = (u \circ s \circ u^{-1}) \cup \{(x, x) | x \in X \text{ and } x \notin u(\omega)\}$. v is a bijection from X to a proper subset of X.

A8.21 Let X be countable. There exists an f: $X >\!\!\longrightarrow \omega$. Let $A \subset X$. Then $(f|A)$: $A >\!\!\longrightarrow \omega$ since $f(x) \in \omega$ implies $(f|A)(x) \in \omega$ and f an injection implies $(f|A)$ is an injection.

A8.22 Given f: $X \longrightarrow\!\!> Y$ and X countable. There exists g: $X >\!\!\longrightarrow \omega$. By the fundamental mapping theorem there exists f_X: $X/S >\!\!\longrightarrow\!\!> Y$. Let χ be a choice function for X. χ: $\mathcal{P}X - \{0\} \to X$ such that $\chi(A) \in A$ for every $A \subset X$, $A \neq \emptyset$. χ: $X/S >\!\!\longrightarrow X$ because $\chi(x/S) = \chi(y/S)$ implies $\chi(x/S) \in y/S$ and $\chi(y/S) \in x/S$, which implies $x/S = y/S$. Hence $g \circ \chi \circ f^{-1}$: $Y >\!\!\longrightarrow \omega$ and Y is countable.

A8.23 Define f: $\omega \times \omega >\!\!\longrightarrow\!\!> \omega$ such that $f(x, y) = (1/2)(x+y)(x+y+1) + y+1$. This function is injective. A proof is as follows:

Case 1. $x + y \neq u + v$. Suppose $x + y > u + v$. Then $x + y \geq u + v + 1$.

$$\begin{aligned}(x+y)(x+y+1)/2 &\geq (u+v+1)(u+v+2)/2 \\ &= (u+v)(u+v+1)/2 + (u+v+1) \\ &\geq (u+v)(u+v+1)/2 + (v+1).\end{aligned}$$

$$(x+y)(x+y+1)/2 + y+1 > (u+v)(u+v+1)/2 + (v+1).$$

A similar argument holds for $x + y < u + v$.

Case 2. $x + y = u + v$ and $y \neq v$. Say $y > v$.

$$(x+y)(x+y+1)/2 + 1 = (u+v)(u+v+1)/2 + 1.$$

$$(x+y)(x+y+1) + y + 1 > (u+v)(u+v+1)/2 + v + 1.$$

Similarly for $y < v$. Hence f is an injection.

Let $n \in \omega$. Since $z(z+1)/2$ is an increasing function, then there exists $z \in \omega$. $z(z+1)/2 \leq n < (z+1)(z+2)/2$.

Let $y = n - 1 - z(z+1)/2$, $x = z - y$. Then $f(x, y) = n$. f is a surjection. $f\colon \omega \times \omega >\!\!\longrightarrow\!\!> \omega$.

Since I is given as a countable set, then

$$\bigcup_{i \in I} A_i = \bigcup_{i \in J} A_i$$

where $J \subset \omega$. A_i is given as countable for each $i \in J$. Let $f_i\colon A_i >\!\!\longrightarrow \omega$ for all $i \in J$. Let $g_i\colon \omega >\!\!\longrightarrow\!\!> \omega \times \{i\}$ for each $i \in \omega$. Then $g_i \circ f_i\colon A_i >\!\!\longrightarrow \omega \times \{i\}$ for all $i \in J$.

$$\bigcup_{i \in J} g_i \circ f_i\colon \bigcup_{i \in J} A_i >\!\!\longrightarrow \omega \times \omega \quad .$$

$$f \circ \Big(\bigcup_{i \in J} g_i \circ f_i \Big)\colon \bigcup_{i \in J} A_i >\!\!\longrightarrow \omega \quad .$$

A8.24 Let $X = \{x\}$. $X \neq \emptyset$. By the axiom of regularity, there is an s such that $s \in X$ and $s \cap X = \emptyset$. $x \cap \{x\} = \emptyset$. $x \notin x$.

A8.25 Let $X = \{x, y\}$. There exists an s such that $s \in X$ and $s \cap X = \emptyset$. $x \cap \{x, y\} = \emptyset$ or $y \cap \{x, y\} = \emptyset$. Suppose $x \in y$ and $y \in x$. Then $x \cap \{x, y\} \neq \emptyset$ and $y \cap \{x, y\} \neq \emptyset$. This is a contradiction.

A8.26 Let $X = \{a_i \mid i \in \omega\}$. There exists an $s \in X$ such that $s \cap X = \emptyset$. There is an a_j such that $a_j \cap \{a_i \mid i \in \omega\} = \emptyset$. But $a_{j+1} \in a_j$ and $a_{j+1} \in \{a_i \mid i \in \omega\}$. Contradiction.

A8.27 $a_i = i$ for example.

A8.28 Suppose $X \neq \emptyset$. Then $X \cup (\bigcup X) \neq \emptyset$. By the axiom of regularity, there exists a set $A \in X \cup (\bigcup X)$ such that $A \cap [X \cup (\bigcup X)] = \emptyset$. If $A \in X$ then $A \in X \times X$. $A = (x, y)$ for some $x \in X$ and $y \in X$. $A \neq \emptyset$. Since $A \in X$ implies $A \subset \bigcup X$, we have $A \cap (\bigcup X) \neq \emptyset$. If $A \in \bigcup X$ then $A \in \bigcup (X \times X)$. $A \in (x, y)$ for some $x \in X$ and $y \in X$. $A = \{x\}$ or $A = \{x, y\}$. $A \cap X \neq \emptyset$. Thus we have in either case $A \cap [X \cup (\bigcup X)] \neq \emptyset$, which is a contradiction.

A9.1 a) $X = \{a, b, c, d, e, f, g\}$; $S = I_X \cup \{(a, b), (a, c), (a, d),$ $(a, e), (a, f), (a, g), (b, d), (b, e), (c, f), (c, g)\}$.

a is the minimum element; d, e, f, g are maximal.

b) $X = \{a, b, c, d, e, f\}$; $S = I_X \cup \{(a, b), (a, c), (a, d),$ $(a, e), (a, f), (d, f), (e, f)\}$.

a is a minimum element; b, c, f are maximal.

A9.2 a)

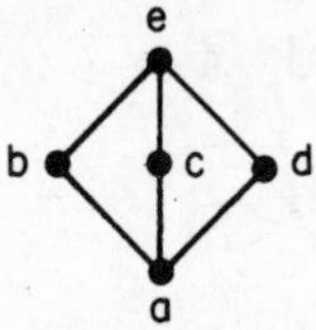

a is the minimum;
e is the maximum.

b)

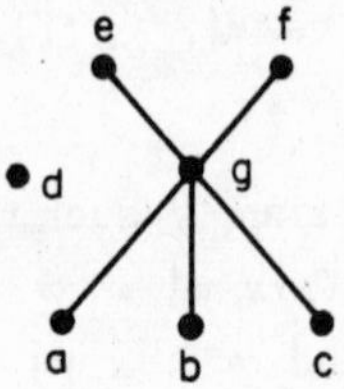

a, b, c are minimal;
e, f are maximal.

c)

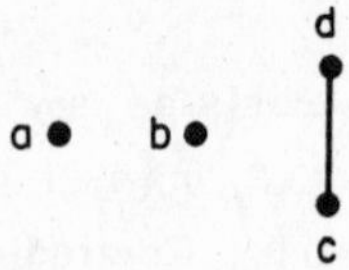

a, b, c are minimal;
a, b, d are maximal.

d)

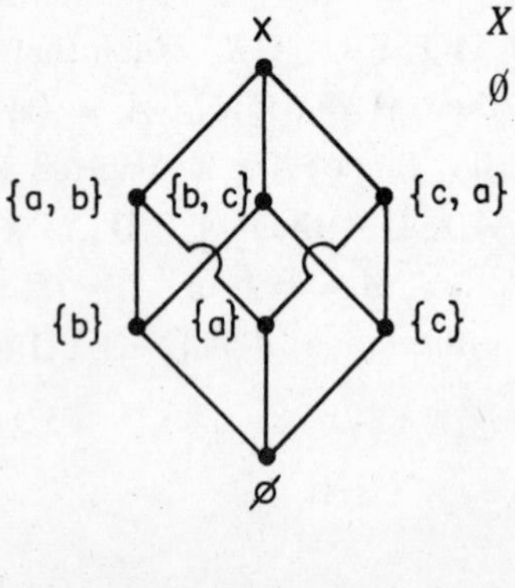

X is the maximum and
$\emptyset$ is the minimum.

A9.3 By check, S is an irreflexive, antisymmetric, and transitive subset of $X \times X$. a and b, for example, are not comparable: neither (a, b) nor (b, a) is a member of S. a, b, d are minimal; c, e are maximal.

A9.4 Let a, b be two distinct minimal elements of X. Now suppose, in order to get a contradiction, that c is a minimum element of X. $c \leq a$ and $c \leq b$. Since a is minimal, one cannot have $c < a$. Therefore $c = a$. Likewise $c = b$. Therefore $a = b$, which is a contradiction. One concludes there can be no minimum element.

A9.5 Let $A = \{a_1, a_2, \ldots, a_n\}$ (designating the members of A as images of members of ω by some bijection). Let $b_1 = a_2 = \text{maximum}\{a_1\}$. Let $b_2 = \text{maximum}\{b_1, a_2\}$. And in general define $b_{i+1} = \text{maximum}\{b_i, a_{i+1}\}$. Thus $b_n = \text{maximum}\{b_{n-1}, a_n\} = \text{maximum } A$. Since maximum A exists it is $\sup A$.

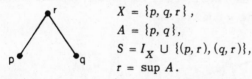

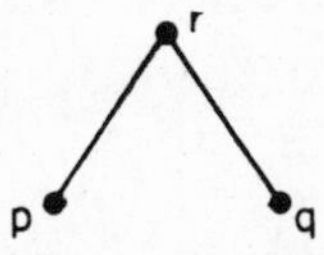

$X = \{p, q, r\}$,

$A = \{p, q\}$,

$S = I_X \cup \{(p, r), (q, r)\}$,

$r = \sup A$.

A9.6 Let $T \in Q$ be a total order on X. Let $S \in Q$ and $T \subset S$. Suppose $(x, y) \in S$. Then $x \in X$ and $y \in X$. Therefore $(x, y) \in T$ or $(y, x) \in T$. If $(y, x) \in T$ then $(y, x) \in S$ and $x = y$. In any case $(x, y) \in T$. $S = T$. Suppose now that S is an order on X which is not total. $(a, b) \notin S$ and $(b, a) \notin S$ for some $a, b \in X$. Define this extension of S: $\overline{S} = \{(x, y) | (x, a) \in S \text{ and } (b, y) \in S\} \cup S$.

$I_X \subset S \subset \overline{S}$ shows $\overline{S}$ to be reflexive. In order to show $\overline{S}$ to be transitive, let (x, y) and $(y, z) \in \overline{S}$.

(i) By cases, if (x, y) and $(y, z) \in S$ then $(x, z) \in S$ and therefore $(x, z) \in \overline{S}$ since $S \subset \overline{S}$.

(ii) If $(x, y) \in S$ and $(y, z) \in S$ and $(b, z) \in S$ then $(x, a) \in S$ and $(b, z) \in S$ yielding $(x, z) \in \overline{S}$.

(iii) If $(x, a) \in S$ and $(b, y) \in S$ and $(y, z) \in S$, then $(x, a) \in S$ and $(b, z) \in S$ yielding $(x, z) \in \overline{S}$.

(iv) If $(x, a) \in S$ and $(b, y) \in S$ and $(y, a) \in S$ and $(b, z) \in S$, then $(x, z) \in \overline{S}$. $\overline{S}$ is transitive.

Now let (x, y) and $(y, x) \in \overline{S}$ and again consider four cases.

(i) $(x, y) \in S$ and $(y, x) \in S$. $x = y$.

(ii) $(x, a) \in S$ and $(b, y) \in S$ and $(y, x) \in S$. $(x, a) \in S$ and $(b, x) \in S$. $(b, a) \in S$ which is a contradiction. This case cannot occur.

(iii) $(x, y) \in S$ and $(y, a) \in S$ and $(b, x) \in S$. $(x, a) \in S$ and $(b, x) \in S$. $(b, a) \in S$. Impossible.

(iv) $(x, a) \in S$ and $(b, y) \in S$ and $(y, a) \in S$ and $(b, x) \in S$. $(b, a) \in S$. This case cannot occur.

Therefore $\overline{S}$ is antisymmetric. We conclude $\overline{S}$ is an order. But $\overline{S}$ properly includes S. Hence S is not maximal.

The orders on 3 are listed in Exercise 3.15's answer. Using those numbers we have this diagram.

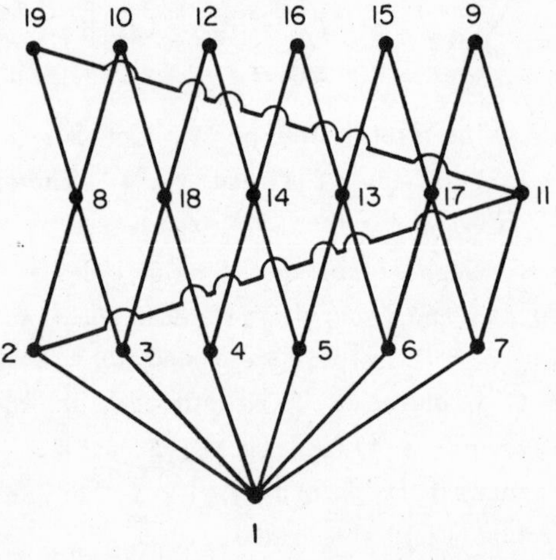

A9.7 For example, let $S = \{(a, b), (b, c), (c, d), (d, a)\}$ and X any set including $\{a, b, c, d\}$.

A9.8 Let a be a lower bound for the nonempty subset B of X. Let A be the set of all lower bounds of B. Any member of B is an upper bound for the set A. Since $B \neq \emptyset$, then A does have an upper bound. Furthermore, A is not empty since $a \in A$. Let $c = \sup A$ (lub A). $c \geq y$ for all $y \in A$. Thus, if c is a lower bound for B, it is the greatest lower bound (inf B). To prove that c is a lower bound for B, suppose, to the contrary, that there exists $d \in B$ such that $d < c$. Then d, as a member of B, is an upper bound for A and is strictly smaller than c, the least upper bound of A. This is a contradiction. c is a lower bound for B. $c =$ glb B.

A9.9 Suppose $f(x) = f(y)$. Then $f(x) \geq f(y)$ yields $x \geq y$ and $f(x) \leq f(y)$ yields $x \leq y$. $x = y$.

A9.10 $x \in \bigcup_{a \in X} s(a)$ implies $x \in s(a)$ for some $a \in X$ which implies $x \in X$. $y \in X$ implies $y \in \bar{s}(y)$ which implies $y \in \bigcup_{a \in X} \bar{s}(a)$. $y \in \bigcup_{a \in X} \bar{s}(a)$ implies $y \in \bar{s}(a)$ for some a which implies $y \in X$. $x \in \bigcap_{a \in X} s(a)$ implies $x < a$ for all $a \in X$ and $x \in X$ which implies $a < a$. Let $m =$ minimum X. $m \leq a$ for all $a \in X$. $m \in \bar{s}(a)$ for all $a \in X$. $m \in \bigcap_{a \in X} \bar{s}(a)$. Now suppose $x \in \bigcap_{a \in X} \bar{s}(a)$. Then $x \leq a$ for all $a \in X$ and $x \in X$. Therefore $x =$ minimum X.

A9.11 $s(a) \leq s(a)$ since $a \leq a$. $s(a) \leq s(b)$ and $s(b) \leq s(a)$ implies $a \leq b$ and $b \leq a$ which implies $a = b$ which implies $s(a) = s(b)$. $s(a) \leq s(b)$ and $s(b) \leq s(c)$ implies $a \leq b$ and $b \leq c$ which implies $a \leq c$ which implies $s(a) \leq s(c)$. $s(a) \leq s(b)$ or $s(b) \leq s(a)$ iff $a \leq b$ or $b \leq a$.

A9.12 and **A9.13** Since $I \neq \emptyset$ let $k \in I$. Then $I_X \subset S_k \subset \bigcup_{i \in I} S_i$. Therefore $\bigcup_{i \in I} S_i$ is reflexive if any S_i is reflexive. $(x, y), (y, x) \in \bigcup_{i \in I} S_i$ implies $(x, y) \in S_j$ and $(y, x) \in S_k$ for some $j, k \in I$. Then (x, y) and $(y, x) \in$ maximum$\{S_j, S_k\}$ since $(S_i)_{i \in I}$ is totally ordered by inclusion. $x = y$. Therefore $\bigcup_{i \in I} S_i$ is antisymmetric if each S_i is antisymmetric.

$$\left(\bigcup_{i \in I} S_i\right)^{-1} = \bigcup_{i \in I} (S_i)^{-1} = \bigcup_{i \in I} S_i \quad .$$

$\bigcup_{i \in I} S_i$ is symmetric if each S_i is symmetric. $(x, y), (y, z) \in \bigcup_{i \in I} S_i$ implies $(x, y) \in S_j$ and $(y, z) \in S_k$ for some j, k. $(x, z) \in \text{maximum}\{S_j, S_k\}$. $(x, z) \in \bigcup_{i \in I} S_i$. $\bigcup_{i \in I} S_i$ is transitive if each S_i is transitive.

A 10.1 There exists an $a_i \in X_i$ for all $i \in n \neq 0$ since $X_i \neq \emptyset$. (i, a_i) is a set since i and a_i are sets (cf. p. 23 of NST). The unordered n-ple (cf. p. 14 of NST), $\{(i, a_i) | i \in n\}$ is a function and a member of $\underset{i \in n}{\mathsf{X}} X_i$.

A 10.2 First if $\mathcal{X}$ is a set, then $\mathcal{P}(\bigcup \mathcal{X})$ is a set. Then $\mathcal{Y} = \{B \mid B \in \mathcal{P}(\bigcup \mathcal{X})$ and $B \subset A$ for some $A \in \mathcal{X}\}$ is a set by the axiom of specification.

Suppose M is maximal for $\mathcal{X}$. Then for all $X \in \mathcal{X}$ we have $M \subset X$ implying $M = X$. $M \in \mathcal{Y}$ since $M \subset M$. Suppose $Y \in \mathcal{Y}$ and $M \subset Y$. But $Y \subset X$ for some $X \in \mathcal{X}$. $M \subset X$. $M = X$. $M = Y$.

Suppose M is maximal for $\mathcal{Y}$. For all $Y \in \mathcal{Y}$: $M \subset Y$ implies $M = Y$. Then $M \subset X$ for some $X \in \mathcal{X}$. Also $X \subset X$ implies $X \in \mathcal{Y}$. Because M is maximal $M = X$. Hence $M \in \mathcal{X}$. M is maximal in $\mathcal{X}$ because $M \subset X$ in $\mathcal{X}$ implies $M \subset X$ in $\mathcal{Y}$ which implies $M = X$.

A 10.3 The given proposition is clearly implied by Zorn's lemma, since $\bigcup \mathcal{C}$ is an upper bound for $\mathcal{C}$ under the inclusion order. The empty chain is bounded by any member of $\mathcal{X}$.

On the other hand, let $X \neq \emptyset$ be a set ordered by $(\leq)$ with every chain $\mathcal{C}$ having an upper bound in X. Let $\mathcal{X}$ be the set of all totally ordered subsets of X. $\mathcal{X} = \emptyset$ since $\emptyset \in \mathcal{X}$. Since the members of $\mathcal{X}$ are subsets of X, $\mathcal{X}$ is ordered by inclusion. Let $\mathcal{C}$ be a nonempty chain $(\subset)$ in $\mathcal{X}$. $\bigcup \mathcal{C} \subset X$. Let

$x, y \in \bigcup\mathcal{C}$. $x \in T_1$, $y \in T_2$ for some $T_1, T_2 \in \mathcal{C}$. Either $T_1 \subset T_2$ or $T_2 \subset T_1$. Let T = maximum$\{T_1, T_2\}$. $x, y \in T$ which is totally ordered. $x \le y$ or $y \le x$. Therefore $\bigcup\mathcal{C}$ is totally ordered and $\bigcup\mathcal{C} \in \mathcal{X}$. Now applying the proposition, there exists an M, a maximal ($\subset$) member of $\mathcal{X}$, that is, a totally ordered subset of X which is maximal with respect to inclusion. Let b be an upper bound for M. b is a maximal element of X, for otherwise suppose some $c \in X$ with $c > b$. $M \cup \{c\}$ is then a properly larger member of $\mathcal{X}$ than is M. This contradicts the maximality of M. $M \cup \{c\}$ is totally ordered because M is totally ordered and $c > b \ge x$ for all $x \in M$.

A 10.4 A proper ideal of R is an ideal of R not equal to R. An ideal A of R is proper iff $1 \notin A$. Proof: If $1 \in A$, then $r \cdot 1 = r \in A$ for all $r \in R$. $A = R$. If $1 \notin A$ then $A \ne R$. Let $\mathcal{X}$ be the set of all proper ideals of R containing a given proper ideal, B. $\mathcal{X}$ is ordered by inclusion. $B \in \mathcal{X}$ implies $\mathcal{X} \ne \emptyset$. Suppose that $\mathcal{C}$ is a nonempty chain in $\mathcal{X}$. Let $x, y \in \bigcup\mathcal{C}$. $x \in A_1$, $y \in A_2$ for some $A_1, A_2 \in \mathcal{C}$. Let A = maximum$\{A_1, A_2\}$. $x, y \in A$. $x - y \in A \subset \bigcup\mathcal{C}$. Let $r \in R$, $x \in \bigcup\mathcal{C}$. $x \in A$ for some $A \in \mathcal{C}$. $rx \in A \subset \bigcup\mathcal{C}$. Hence $\bigcup\mathcal{C}$ is an ideal of R. Suppose $1 \in \bigcup\mathcal{C}$. Then $1 \in A$ for some $A \in \mathcal{C}$. This is a contradiction since A is a proper ideal. Therefore $1 \notin \bigcup\mathcal{C}$ and $\bigcup\mathcal{C}$ is a proper ideal. $B \subset A$ for each A in C implies $B \subset \bigcup\mathcal{C}$. $\bigcup\mathcal{C} \in \mathcal{X}$. By Zorn's lemma $\mathcal{X}$ has a maximal element, i.e., a maximal proper ideal of R containing a given ideal B.

A 10.5 Let V be a vector space. Let F be its field. Let $\mathcal{X}$ be the set of all linearly independent subsets of V. A subset of V is linearly independent if $\Sigma_{i \in n} k_i \vec{x}_i = \vec{0}$ implies $k_i = 0$ for all $i \in n$; $\vec{x}_i \in A$, $k_i \in F$, $n \in \omega$.

$\emptyset \in \mathcal{X}$ implies $\mathcal{X} \ne \emptyset$. $\mathcal{X}$ is ordered by inclusion. Let $\mathcal{C}$ be a nonempty chain. Let $\vec{x}_i \in \bigcup\mathcal{C}$ for all $i \in n$ such that $\Sigma_{i \in n} k_i \vec{x}_i = \vec{0}$. There exist $A_0, A_1, \ldots, A_{n-1} \in \mathcal{C}$ such that

$\vec{x}_i \in A_i$. Let $A \in \mathcal{C}$, $A = \text{maximum}\{A_0, A_1, \ldots, A_{n-1}\}$ by the total ordering of $\mathcal{C}$. $\vec{x}_i \in A$ for all $i \in n$. Therefore $k_i = 0$ for all $i \in n$ and $\bigcup \mathcal{C}$ is linearly independent. Let M be a maximal linearly independent set. That a maximal linearly independent subset of V is a basis for V is a theorem of linear algebra. For a discussion of linear independence and bases of vector spaces which have finite bases see P. Halmos' *Finite Dimensional Vector Spaces.*

A 10.6 An order is total iff it is maximal. Cf. Exercise 9.6. Now let $\mathfrak{X} = \{S \mid S$ is an order on X and $T \subset S\}$. $T \in \mathfrak{X}$ implies $\mathfrak{X} \neq \emptyset$. If $\mathcal{C} \neq \emptyset$ is a chain of orders including T, then $\bigcup \mathcal{C}$ includes T and by Exercise 9.13, is an order. Thus by Zorn's lemma, $\mathfrak{X}$ contains a maximal element. A maximal element of $\mathfrak{X}$ is a total order including T.

A 10.7 Let $\mathfrak{E} = \{E \mid \mathbf{Q} \subsetneq E \subset \mathbf{R}$; E is the domain of a function F agreeing with the identity on $\mathbf{Q}$, if $x \in E$, $y \in E$, $x+y \in E$, then $F(x+y) = F(x) + F(y)\}$. $\mathbf{Q} \cup \{\pi\}$ is the domain of the function $I_{\mathbf{Q}} \cup \{(\pi, 0)\}$ and therefore belongs to $\mathfrak{E}$. $\mathfrak{E}$ is, therefore, nonempty. Now let $\mathcal{C}$ be a chain in $\mathfrak{E}$. $\bigcup \mathcal{C}$ is the domain of $\bigcup_{\text{dom } F \in \mathcal{C}} F$. Use Zorn's lemma. Let M be a maximal set in $\mathfrak{E}$ and suppose $M \neq \mathbf{R}$. Let $a \in \mathbf{R} - M$. M is a proper subset of $M \cup \{a\}$. To obtain a contradiction, show $M \cup \{a\} \in \mathfrak{E}$.

Case 1. $x + a \in M$ for some $x \in M$. Define $F(a) = F(x+a) - F(x)$. Then for $y + a \in M$, $y \in M$, one has

$$\begin{aligned}
F(y+a+x) &= F(x+a+y).\\
F(y+a) + F(x) &= F(x+a) + F(y).\\
F(y+a) &= F(x) + F(a) + F(y) - F(x)\\
&= F(y) + F(a).
\end{aligned}$$

Case 2. $x + a \notin M$ for any $x \in M$. Define $F(a) = 0$.

A 10.8 Given *ZL*. Prove *KL*. Let $(X, \leq)$ be given. Let C be a given chain in X. Let $(\mathfrak{X}, \subset)$ be the ordered set of all chains in X which include C. $C \in \mathfrak{X}$. Let $\mathcal{C} \neq \emptyset$ be an inclusion chain of members of $\mathfrak{X}$. $\bigcup \mathcal{C} \in \mathfrak{X}$ also since $x, y \in \bigcup \mathcal{C}$ imply $x \in A \in \mathcal{C}$

and $y \in B \in \mathcal{C}$ for some A, B. But $A \subset B$ or $B \subset A$. Thus $x \leq y$ or $y \leq x$. $\bigcup\mathcal{C}$ is a chain. $C \subset A \subset \bigcup\mathcal{C}$. $\bigcup\mathcal{C} \in \mathcal{X}$. $\mathcal{C} \neq \emptyset$ has an upper bound in $\mathcal{X}$. $\mathcal{X}$ has a maximal element M. $C \subset M$. Given *KL*. Prove *ZL*. *ZL* in the form given in Exercise 10.3 will be proved. Let $\mathcal{X} \neq \emptyset$ be a set of sets. Let every chain ($\subset$) have $\bigcup\mathcal{C} \in \mathcal{X}$. Since $\mathcal{X} \neq \emptyset$, then $A \in \mathcal{X}$ for some A. $\{A\}$ is a chain and is included in a maximal chain $\mathfrak{D}$. $M = \bigcup\mathfrak{D} \in \mathcal{X}$. M is maximal in $\mathcal{X}$ for otherwise let $Q \supsetneq M$. Then $\mathfrak{D} \cup \{Q\}$ is strictly larger than $\mathfrak{D}$, which is impossible.

A 10.9 Given *AC*. Prove *ZP*. Let f be a choice function for $\mathcal{P}(\bigcup\mathcal{X})$. $A \in X$ implies $A \in \mathcal{P}(\bigcup\mathcal{X})$. Then $f(X) \in X$. Define F = image f. Then $p \in X \cap F$ iff $p \in X$ and $p \in F$ iff $p \in X$ and $p = f(A)$ for some A iff $p = f(X)$. Therefore $X \cap F = \{f(X)\}$, a singleton.

Given *ZP*. Prove *AC*. Let $\mathsf{X}_{i \in I \neq \emptyset} X_i$ with $X_i \neq \emptyset$ be given. Let $A_i = \{i\} \times X_i$ for each $i \in I$. Let $\mathcal{X} = \{A_i | i \in I\}$. $A_i \neq \emptyset$ for each $i \in I$, because suppose $A_i = \emptyset$. $\{i\} \times X_i = \emptyset$. $X_i = \emptyset$.

Now suppose $i \neq j$. Then $A_i \cap A_j = \emptyset$. Thus $\mathcal{X}$ is a nonempty set of disjoint nonempty sets. By *ZP* there exists an F such that $A \cap F$ is a singleton for each $i \in I$. Define $G = F \cap I \times \bigcup_{i \in I} X_i$. Now G has these properties: $G \subset I \times \bigcup_{i \in I} X_i$; for each $i \in I$ there exists $(i, x_i) \in G$; $(i, x_i) \in G$ and $(i, y_i) \in G$ imply $x_i = y_i$; $(i, x_i) \in G$ implies $x_i \in X_i$. Thus $G \in \mathsf{X}_{i \in I} X_i$.

A 11.1 Let $y \in A$. $y \in$ image $(T \cap (\{a\} \times A))$ iff $(x, y) \in T \cap (\{a\} \times A)$ for some $x \in X$ if $(a, y) \in T$. A = image $(T \cap (\{a\} \times A))$ iff $(a, y) \in T$ for all $y \in A$ iff a is the minimum element of A.

A11.2 By the axiom of specification, f is a set. Since f is a choice function, this is a proof that the well ordering theorem implies the axiom of choice.

A11.3 A nonempty subset of a subset of a well ordered set is a nonempty subset of a well ordered set and therefore has a minimum element.

A11.4 $(<_2)$ is stronger than $(<_1)$, $(<_4)$ is stronger than $(<_3)$, $(<_2)$, and $(<_1)$. $(<_3)$ is stronger than $(<_1)$.

A11.5 Let $s(c)$ be an initial segment of $s(a)$ which is an initial segment of X.

$$\begin{aligned} s(c) &= \{x \mid x \in s(a) \text{ and } x < c \text{ and } c \in s(a)\} \\ &= \{x \mid x \in X \text{ and } x < a \text{ and } x < c \text{ and } c \in X\} \\ &= \{x \mid x \in X \text{ and } x < c \text{ and } c \in X\} \quad \text{since } c < a. \end{aligned}$$

Let $s(c)$ be an initial segment of X.

$$s(c) = \{x \mid x \in X \text{ and } x < c \text{ and } c \in X\}.$$
$$s(a) = \{x \mid x \in X \text{ and } x < a \text{ and } a \in X\}.$$

If $c < a$ then

$$\begin{aligned} s(c) &= \{x \mid x \in X \text{ and } x < c \text{ and } c \in X\} \\ &= \{x \mid x \in s(a) \text{ and } x < c \text{ and } c \in s(a)\}. \end{aligned}$$

If $c \geq a$ then

$$s(a) = \{x \mid x \in X \text{ and } x < a\} \subset \{x \mid x \in X \text{ and } x < c\} = s(c).$$

A11.7 Consider $(\omega, \leq)$, where $(\leq)$ is the established order. Since $(\omega, \leq)$ has no maximal element, $(\omega, (\leq)^{-1})$ has no minimal element. $(\leq)$ is total and therefore $(\leq)^{-1}$ is total. A total order is maximal, and therefore $(\leq)^{-1} \subset T$ implies $(\leq)^{-1} = T$. Of course since $(\leq)^{-1}$ has no minimal element, it is not a well ordering.

A11.8 Let (X, T) be a totally ordered set. Let $\mathfrak{W} = \{(W, S_W) \mid W \subset X \text{ and } S_W \text{ is a well ordering and } S_W \subset T\}$. $(\emptyset, \emptyset) \in \mathfrak{W}$ implies $\mathfrak{W} \neq \emptyset$. $\mathfrak{W}$ is ordered by continuation. If $\mathcal{C}$ is a chain in $\mathfrak{W}$

then $\bigcup\mathcal{C} \in \mathcal{W}$. $\mathcal{W}$ has a maximal element (F, S_F). F is cofinal provided for all $x \in X$ there exists an $a \in F$ such that $(x, a) \in T$.

Suppose for some $x_1 \in X$ it is not the case that there is an $a \in F$ such that $(x_1, a) \in T$. Since X is totally ordered by T; $(a, x_1) \in T$ for all $a \in F$. Then $F' = F \cup \{x_1\}$ with the order $S_{F'} = S_F \cup \{(a, x_1) | a \in F\} \cup \{(x_1, x_1)\}$ is a well ordered continuation of (F, S_F) contradicting its maximality.

A 11.9 Let a be the first element of the well ordered set X. Then $s(a) = \emptyset$, which is clearly a subset of S. It follows that $a \in S$.

A 12.1 In the notation of the transfinite recursion theorem (p. 70, NST) let $W = \omega$ and define f as follows: $f((x_i)_{i \in 0}) = a_0$, $f((x_i)_{i \in 1}) = a_1, \ldots, f((x_i)_{i \in n-1}) = a_{n-1}$, $f((x_i)_{i \in n}) = F(x_{n-N}, x_{n-N+1}, \ldots, x_{n-2}, x_{n-2})$, $n \geq N$. The conclusion follows as stated in the exercise.

A 12.2 $N = 2$, $a_0 = 0$, $a_1 = 1$,

$$F(x_{n-2}, x_{n-1}) = \frac{-A(x)(k-1)a_{k-1} + B(x)a_{k-2}}{k(k-1)} .$$

A 12.3 Exercise 8.4 and Peano axiom V and exercise p. 49 of NST.

A 12.4 Let $y_1, y_2 \in Y$. $y_1 = f(x_1)$ and $y_2 = f(x_2)$ for some $x_1, x_2 \in X$. $x_1 \leq x_2$ or $x_2 \leq x_1$. $f(x_1) \leq f(x_2)$ or $f(x_2) \leq f(x_1)$. $y_1 \leq y_2$ or $y_2 \leq y_1$. Y is totally ordered.

Let $B \neq \emptyset$ be a subset of Y. $A = f^{-1}(B)$ is a nonempty subset of X. A has a minimum element a. $a \leq x$ for all $x \in A$. $f(a) \leq f(x)$ for all $x \in A$. $f(a) \leq y$ for all $y \in B$. $f(a)$ is the minimum element of B.

A 12.5 Suppose $x_1 < x_2$ iff $f(x_1) < f(x_2)$. $x_1 \leq x_2$ means $x_1 < x_2$ and $x_1 = x_2$. This is equivalent to $f(x_1) < f(x_2)$ and $f(x_1) = f(x_2)$. This means $f(x_1) \leq f(x_2)$.

On the other hand, suppose $x_1 \leq x_2$ iff $f(x_1) \leq f(x_2)$. Now $x_1 < x_2$ means $x_1 \leq x_2$ and $x_1 \neq x_2$. This is equivalent to $f(x_1) \leq f(x_2)$ and $f(x_1) \neq f(x_2)$, which means $f(x_1) < f(x_2)$.

A 12.6 The implication "if $f(x_1) \leq f(x_2)$ then $x_1 \leq x_2$" must be proved. Suppose not $(x_1 \leq x_2)$. Then, since X is totally ordered, $x_2 < x_1$. $f(x_2) < f(x_1)$. (Why?) It is then not the case that $f(x_1) \leq f(x_2)$.

A 12.7 The composition of two similarities is a similarity. I_X is a similarity. The inverse of a similarity is a similarity. Thus, the set of similarities of X together with composition is a group. Since every similarity is a bijection, the similarity group is a subgroup of the symmetric group.

A 12.8 Let $a = \sup A$. $a \geq x$ for all $x \in A$. $f(a) \geq f(x)$ for all $x \in A$. $f(a) \geq y$ for all $y \in f(A)$. Therefore $f(a)$ is an upper bound for $f(A)$. Let $b \geq y$ for all $y \in f(A)$. $f^{-1}(b) \geq x$ for all $x \in A$. $f^{-1}(b) \geq a$ since $a = \sup A$. $b \geq f(a)$. Therefore $f(a) = \sup f(A)$.

A 12.9 Any similarity of a well ordered set onto a subset of itself must satisfy the inequality $x \leq f(x)$ for all $x \in \omega$. The only possible values of n are therefore 2, 3, 4.

A 12.10 Let $f\colon \omega >\!\!\longrightarrow\!\!> \omega$ be a similarity. Suppose $f(0) = k > 0$. Then $f(i) = 0$ for some $i \in \omega$. $i \neq 0$ since $f(0) = k > 0$. One then has $i > 0$ and $f(i) < f(0)$ which contradicts f's being a similarity. Therefore $f(0) = 0$. Define $S = \{n \mid n \in \omega \text{ and } f(n) = n\}$. It was just proven that $0 \in S$. Assume $n \in S$. $f(n) = n$. If $f(n^+) \neq n^+$, then

a) $f(n^+) = n$, which is impossible since $f(n) = n$;

b) $f(n^+) < n$, which is impossible because then $n < n^+$

and $f(n) > f(n^+)$;

c) $f(n^+) = k > n^+$. Let j be such that $f(j) = n^+$. If $j < n$, then $f(j) = n^+ > f(n)$ gives a contradiction. If $j > n^+$, then $f(j) < f(n^+)$ gives a contradiction.

Therefore we have $n^+ \in S$. $f = I_\omega$.

A briefer argument is to note that the identity mapping is a similarity and that similarities from well ordered sets to well ordered sets are unique.

A 12.11 Let f be a similarity, $f\colon \mathbf{Z} >\!\!\longrightarrow\!\!> \mathbf{Z}$. $f(0) = m$ for some $m \in \mathbf{Z}$. Now by an induction similar to the one in 12.9 prove first that $f(n) = m + n$ for $n \geq 0$ $(n \in \omega)$. By another induction prove that $f(-n) = m + (-n)$ for $n \in \omega$.

A 12.12 To each member $a \in \mathbf{Z}$ corresponds the member h_a of $\mathfrak{S}(\mathbf{Z})$, where $h_a(x) = x + a$. That these bijections are the only similarities of $\mathbf{Z}$ was shown in 12.10. Therefore $\Phi\colon \mathbf{Z} >\!\!\longrightarrow\!\!> \mathcal{S}(\mathbf{Z})$ is the similarity subgroup of $\mathbf{Z}$. Define $h_a > h_b$ iff $h_a(x) > h_b(x)$ for all $x \in \mathbf{Z}$. Note $a > b$ iff $x + a > x + b$ for all $x \in \mathbf{Z}$ iff $h_a(x) > h_b(x)$ for all $x \in \mathbf{Z}$, and therefore Φ is a similarity.

A 12.13 Let $a > 0$. Then $x_1 \geq x_2$ implies $ax_1 \geq ax_2$ which implies $ax_1 + b \geq ax_2 + b$ which implies $f(x_1) \geq f(x_2)$.

$F\colon \mathbf{R} >\!\!\longrightarrow\!\!> \mathbf{R}$ such that
$F(x) = x$ for $x < 0$
$F(x) = 2x$ for $x \geq 0$ is a similarity.

A 12.14 Cf. 4.17 and 3.32 in which are defined the bijection Φ and the order *is finer than*. Let $S \subset T$. $z \in x/S$ implies $(z, x) \in S$ which implies $(z, x) \in T$ which in turn implies $z \in x/T$. Hence, given X/S and $x/S \in X/S$, there exists an $x/T \in X/T$ such that $x/S \subset x/T$. Thus X/S is finer than X/T. Now on the other hand, let X/S be finer than X/T. Let $(z, x) \in S$. Given X/S and $x/S \in X/S$, we have $x/S \subset v$ for some $v \in X/T$. $v = x/T$ since $x \in v$. $x/S \subset x/T$. $z \in x/S$ implies $z \in x/T$. $(z, x) \in T$. $S \subset T$.

A 12.15 E is ordered by inclusion. Let $S, T \in E$. $\sup\{S, T\} = \bigcap\{R \mid R \in E \text{ and } S \subset R \text{ and } T \subset R\}$, $\inf\{S, T\} = S \cap T$ are easily shown to be members of E. Thus E is a lattice. A similar construction will also show E to be a complete lattice. For the partitions use 12.14 and 12.8.

A 12.16 $(x_1, x_2) \in R$ iff $(f(x_2), f(x_1)) \in S$ iff $(f(x_1), f(x_2)) \in S^{-1}$.

A 12.17 $f\colon X >\!\!\longrightarrow\!\!> Y$ is a similarity of the ordered sets (X, R), (Y, S^{-1}) and (X, R) well ordered imply (Y, S^{-1}) is well ordered. Cf. 12.4.

A 12.18 $(x_1, x_2) \in R$ iff $(f(x_1), f(x_2)) \in S$.
$(x_2, x_1) \in R^{-1}$ iff $(f(x_2), f(x_1)) \in S^{-1}$.

A 12.19 On page 72 of NST it is proven that a similarity from one well ordered set to another is unique. If (X, R) is well ordered, then (Y, S) is also and f is unique. If (Y, S) is well ordered, then (X, R) is also and f is unique. f is a similarity from (X, R^{-1}) to (Y, S^{-1}). If (X, R^{-1}) is well ordered, then (Y, S^{-1}) is also and f is unique. If (Y, S^{-1}) is well ordered, then (X, R^{-1}) is also and f is unique.

A 12.20 a is a minimum element of a subset A iff $(a, x) \in S$ for all $x \in A$. a is a maximum element of a subset A iff $(x, a) \in S$ for all $x \in A$. Thus a is a minimum element with respect to the order S iff it is a maximum element with respect to the order S^{-1}. (X, S) is doubly well ordered iff every nonempty subset A has a minimum and a maximum element with respect to S iff every nonempty subset A has a minimum element with respect to S and a minimum element with respect to S^{-1} iff (X, S) and (X, S^{-1}) are well ordered. Let X be doubly well ordered. Given two well ordered sets, ω and X (infinite), either they are similar or there exists a similarity of ω to an initial segment of X (cf. p. 73, NST). Let $f\colon \omega >\!\!\longrightarrow X$. Since $f(\omega)$ is doubly well ordered, so is ω (proof?). But ω has no maximum element. Therefore if X is infinite it cannot be doubly well ordered.

A 12.21 Suppose there exists an antisimilarity f of ω to itself. Let $f(0) = k$. Then $f(1), f(2), \ldots, f(k), f(k+1)$ all are distinct images and must all be strictly less than $f(0) = k$. This is impossible.

$F(x) = -x + k$ is an antisimilarity of $\mathbf{Z}$.

$f(x) = k/x$ with $k \in (0, \infty)$ is an antisimilarity of $(0, \infty)$.

A 12.22 f: $[0, 1] >\!\!-\!\!\!> [0, 1)$ such that $f(x) = x/2$; g: $[0, 1) >\!\!-\!\!\!> [0, 1]$ such that $g(x) = x$. But $[0, 1]$ and $[0, 1)$, real intervals, are not similar as $[0, 1)$ has no last element.

A 13.1 In a given nonempty set of successor sets there is a maximal member. Let $\mathcal{S}$ be a nonempty set of successor sets. $\mathcal{S}$ is ordered by inclusion. Let $\mathcal{C} \neq 0$ be a chain of successor sets. $0 \in X$ for each $X \in \mathcal{C}$ and therefore $0 \in \bigcup\mathcal{C}$. Let $n \in \bigcup\mathcal{C}$. $n \in X$ for some $X \in \mathcal{C}$. Since X is a successor set, $n^+ \in X$ and therefore $n^+ \in \bigcup\mathcal{C}$. By Zorn's lemma there exists a maximal member of $\mathcal{S}$.

There is not a largest successor set; consider this argument. Let C be any successor set. For every $n \in \omega$ define the n-th successor of C, $C^{(n)}$, by induction: if $n = 0$ then $C^{(n)} = C$, $C^{(n)} = D$ implies $C^{(n^+)} = D^+$. In the notation of the axiom of substitution (p. 75 of NST) let $A = \omega$, $S(a, b) = a \in \omega$ and $b \in C^{(a)}$. Thus there exists an F with domain ω and with value $F(n) = C^{(n)}$. The image $F = \{C^{(n)} \mid n \in \omega\}$ is then a set. Call it E. Consider $C \cup E$. $0 \in C$ implies $0 \in C \cup E$. Let $x \in C \cup E$. Then $x \in C$ or $x \in E$. If $x \in C$, then $x^+ \in C$ which yields $x^+ \in C \cup E$. If on the other hand $x \in E$, then $x = C^{(n)}$ for some $n \in \omega$. $x^+ = C^{(n^+)}$. $x^+ \in E$. $x^+ \in C \cup E$. Therefore $C \cup E$ is a successor set such that $C \subsetneqq C \cup E$. There can be no largest successor set.

A 13.2 Let X be a set and $s(x)$ a condition (either true or false for each member of X). Then $Y = \{x \mid x \in X \text{ and } s(x)\}$ is a set.

For case 1 suppose $s(a)$ for some $a \in X$. Let $F(x) = \{b \mid (s(x)$ and $x \in X$ and $b \in x)$ or (not $(s(x))$ and $x \in X$ and $b \in a)\}$. $F(x)$ will have either the value x (if $s(x)$) or the value a (if not $s(x)$). In either case the value is a set. Furthermore $F(x) = a$ for at least one member of X, namely, a. By the axiom of substitution, F is a function and the image of F, $F(X)$ is a set. $y \in F(X)$ iff $y \in X$ and $s(y)$. For case 2 suppose not $(s(x))$ for all $x \in X$. Then: if $x \in X$, then not $(x \in X$ and $s(x))$, yielding $x \notin Y$. On the other hand if $x \notin X$, then not $(x \in X$ and $s(x))$, yielding again $x \notin Y$. Therefore $x \notin Y$ for all x. $Y = \emptyset$.

A 13.3 Let sets X, Y be given. Let $A = \{0, 1\} = \{\emptyset, \{\emptyset\}\} = \mathcal{P}\mathcal{P}\emptyset$. $S(a, b) = (a = 0$ and $b \in X)$ or $(a = 1$ and $b \in Y)$. $\{b \mid S(0, b)\} = X$ and $\{b \mid S(1, b)\} = Y$, both given sets. By the axiom of substitution there exists a function F with domain 2. Image $F = F(2) = \{X, Y\}$ is a set.

A 13.4 First, let α be an ordinal. α is a well ordered set and if $\zeta \in \alpha$ then $\xi = \{x \mid x \in \alpha$ and $x < \xi\}$. Let $x \in \alpha$. Then $x = s(x)$ which is a subset of α. Therefore $x \in \alpha$ implies $x \subset \alpha$. Now let $x, y \in \alpha$. $x \in y$ iff $x \in s(y)$ iff $x < y$. Since $(<)$ well orders α, (ϵ) does also. $(\epsilon) = (<)$. α is well ordered by (ϵ) and $x \in \alpha$ implies $x \subset \alpha$.

Second, let α be well ordered by (ϵ) and $x \in \alpha$ imply $x \subset \alpha$. Let $\xi \in \alpha$. $\xi \cap \alpha = \{x \mid x \in \alpha$ and $x \in \xi\}$. But since $\xi \in \alpha$ implies $\xi \subset \alpha$ one has $\xi \cap \alpha = \xi = \{x \mid x \in \alpha$ and $x \in \xi\} = s_\epsilon(\xi)$. Hence α is a well ordered set (ordered by ϵ) such that for all $\xi \in \alpha$, $\xi = \{x \mid x \in \alpha$ and $x < \xi\}$.

A 13.5 Let $\xi \in \alpha$. $\xi \cap \alpha = \{x \mid x \in \alpha$ and $x \in \xi\}$. But $\xi \in \alpha$ implies $\xi \subset \alpha$. Therefore $\xi \cap \alpha = \xi = \{x \mid x \in \alpha$ and $x \in \xi\}$. $\xi = s_\epsilon(\xi)$. To show that α is well ordered, let $\beta \neq \emptyset$. By the axiom of regularity there exists a $\gamma \in \beta$ such that $\gamma \cap \beta = \emptyset$. Let $y \in \beta$. Then since β is totally ordered, $y \in \gamma$ or $y = \gamma$ or $\gamma \in y$. Suppose $y \in \gamma$. But $y \in \beta$ and $\gamma \cap \beta \neq \emptyset$. Contradiction.

Therefore $y = \gamma$ or $\gamma \in y$. γ is the minimum of β. α is well ordered.

A 13.6 If $\beta < \alpha^+$ then $\beta \in \alpha \cup \{\alpha\}$. Then $\beta \in \alpha$ or $\beta = \alpha$. In either case one cannot have $\alpha \in \beta$. See p. 79 of NST.

A 13.7 If $\alpha \in \alpha$ then $s(\alpha) = \alpha$ is an initial segment of itself. But a well ordered set cannot be similar to an initial segment of itself.

A 13.8 Let x be a set such that $x \in \alpha$ and $\alpha \subset x$. x is an ordinal since $x \in \alpha$. If $\alpha \subset x$ then $\alpha = x$ or $\alpha \in x$. Neither are possible, since α and x are ordinals and $x \in \alpha$, remembering that the set of ordinals $\{\alpha, x\}$ is strictly and totally ordered by $\in$.

A 13.9 ω is an ordinal iff ω is well ordered by $(\in)$ and $x \in \omega$ implies $x \subset \omega$. These are theorems already proven.

A 13.10 Every member of the ordinal ω is an ordinal.

A 13.11 Let α be an ordinal. $\alpha^+ = \alpha \cup \{\alpha\}$ is an ordinal which contains α. Furthermore $\alpha = s(\alpha)$ in α^+.

A 13.12 Let A be a nonempty set of ordinals. Let $\alpha \in A$. If α is the smallest member of A, then denote this minimum A by β; i.e., $\beta = \alpha$. If, on the other hand, $\alpha \neq \min A$, then consider $\alpha \cap A$. $\alpha \cap A \neq 0$ and is well ordered. Let β be the smallest member of $\alpha \cap A$. Note that if $\gamma \in A$ and $\gamma \in \beta$, then since $\beta \in \alpha$ we have $\gamma \in \alpha$ yielding $\gamma \in \alpha \cap A$, contradicting β's being the smallest member. Thus β is the smallest member of A. A, an arbitrary nonempty set of ordinals, has a least member β. If $x \in \beta$ then $x \in \gamma$ for all $\gamma \in A$. Therefore $\beta \subset \bigcap A$. But since $\beta \in A$, we have $\bigcap A \subset \beta$. Thus $\bigcap A$ is an ordinal and is the smallest ordinal in A.

A 13.13 Suppose α to be a limit ordinal. Then there is no ordinal β such that $\beta^+ = \alpha$. $x \in \alpha$ implies $x \subset \alpha$ and therefore $x^+ = x \cup \{x\} \subset \alpha$. If $x \in \alpha$ and $x^+ = \alpha$, then α is not a limit ordinal.

Therefore we must have $x \in a$ implying $x^+ \subsetneq a$. But x^+ is an ordinal and therefore $x^+ \in a$. We have $x \in a$ implying $x \in x^+ \in a$. Thus if $x \in a$ then $x \in \bigcup a$, $a \subset \bigcup a$. But clearly $y \in \bigcup a$ implies $y \in p \in a$, which implies $y \in p \subset a$, which implies $y \in a$, which implies $\bigcup a \subset a$. $\bigcup a = a$.

Now suppose a not to be a limit ordinal. Then since a is not zero, $a = \beta^+$ for some ordinal β. $\beta \in a$. To prove $\beta \notin \bigcup a$ assume $\beta \in \bigcup a$ and obtain a contradiction as follows. $\beta \in k \in a$. $\beta \in k \in \beta \cup \{\beta\}$. $\beta \in k \in \beta$ implies $\beta \in k \subset \beta$ which implies $\beta \in \beta$, a contradiction. $\beta \in k = \beta$ implies $\beta \in \beta$, the contradiction. Thus with $\beta \notin \bigcup a$ and $\beta \in a$ we have $a \neq \bigcup a$.

A 13.14 Let $x \in \bigcup a^+$. $x \in k \in a^+$. $x \in k \in a$ or $x \in k = a$. $x \in a$. On the other hand let $x \in a$. $x \in a \in \{a\}$. $x \in a \in a^+$. $x \in \bigcup a^+$. $a = \bigcup a^+$.

A 13.15 If a is a limit ordinal then $a = \bigcup a$. If a is not a limit ordinal, then $a = 0$ or $a = \gamma^+$ for some ordinal γ. If $a = 0$, then $\beta < 0$ implies $\beta < \bigcup 0$. If $a = \gamma^+$, then $\bigcup a = \bigcup \gamma^+ = \gamma$. But $\beta < a$ implies $\beta \leq \gamma = \bigcup a$. If $a = \bigcup a$ then $\beta < a$ implies $\beta \leq \bigcup a$.

A 13.16 If a is a finite set, then $a \sim n$ for some $n \in \omega$. If two set are ordinals, then a is similar to an initial segment of n or n is similar to an initial segment of a or $a = n$. But any similarity is an equivalence. The only possibility is $a = n$.

A 13.17 $(X, \leq)$ is well ordered and is therefore similar to some ordinal. This ordinal must be finite, a natural number, for by composition it is equivalent to a natural number.

A 13.18 Let $W = \{A \mid (A$ is an initial segment of X or $A = X)$ and A is similar to some ordinal$\}$. Since $\emptyset = s(\text{minimum } X)$ is similar to 0 we have $W \neq \emptyset$. Let $\mathcal{C}$ be a chain of initial segments of X, each similar to an ordinal. By the axiom of substitution, the ordinals similar to members of $\mathcal{C}$ form a set S. $\bigcup \mathcal{C} = \sup \mathcal{C}$. $\bigcup \mathcal{C}$ is similar to $\sup S$. Hence $\bigcup \mathcal{C} \in W$. W has a maximal element M which is similar to some ordinal μ. This by Zorn's lemma. If $M \neq X$ then let $a = \text{minimum}(X - M)$. $M \cup \{a\}$ is a well ordered subset of X and is similar to μ^+, contradicting the maximality of M.

A 13.19 Let ϵ_α be the order on the ordinal α. Since α and 0 are disjoint well ordered sets, the ordinal sum is the set $\alpha \cup 0$ with the order $\epsilon_\alpha \cup (\alpha \times 0) \cup \epsilon_0$. This well ordered set is exactly the ordinal α. In like manner $0 + \alpha = \alpha$ is proven.

A 13.20 $\{\alpha\}$ with order $\{(\alpha, \alpha)\}$ is a well ordered set similar to $1 = \{0\}$ with order $\{(0, 0)\}$. Furthermore $\{\alpha\}$ and α are disjoint. Hence $\alpha + 1$ is the unique ordinal similar to $\alpha \cup \{\alpha\}$ with the well ordering $\epsilon_\alpha \cup (\epsilon_\alpha \times \{\alpha\}) \cup \{(\alpha, \alpha)\}$, or more simply, the ordinal α^+.

A 13.21 $1 + \omega = \omega$.

A 13.22 $1 + 0 = 0^+$.

A 13.23 Suppose α, β, γ are respectively similar to the disjoint well ordered sets $(A, R), (B, S), (C, T)$. $B \cup C$ has order $S \cup (B \times C) \cup T$ and is similar to $\beta + \gamma$. $A \cup (B \cup C)$ has order $R \cup [A \times (B \cup C)] \cup [S \cup (B \times C) \cup T]$ and is similar to $\alpha + (\beta + \gamma)$. $(A \cup B) \cup C$ has order $(R \cup (A \times B) \cup S) \cup [(A \cup B) \times C] \cup T$ and is similar to $(\alpha + \beta) + \gamma$. But $A \cup (B \cup C) = (A \cup B) \cup C$ and $R \cup [A \times (B \cup C)] \cup [S \cup (B \times C) \cup T] = [R \cup (A \times B) \cup S] \cup [(A \cup B) \times C] \cup T$. Therefore $\alpha + (\beta + \gamma)$ is similar to $(\alpha + \beta) + \gamma$ and hence equal.

A 13.24 Suppose $\alpha < \beta$. Then α is an initial segment of β. $\beta - \alpha$, the relative complement, is a well ordered nonempty subset of β, and is similar to some ordinal $\gamma \neq 0$. $\alpha + \gamma$ is similar to the ordinal sum of the disjoint well ordered sets α and $\beta - \alpha$, namely, β with the order $\epsilon_\alpha \cup [\alpha \times (\beta - \alpha)] \cup \epsilon_{\beta - \alpha} = \epsilon_\beta$. Suppose $\alpha + \gamma = \beta$ with $\gamma \neq 0$. If (A, R) and (C, T) are disjoint well ordered sets similar respectively to α and γ, then $((A \cup C), R \cup (A \times C) \cup T)$ is a well ordered set similar to β by some bijection f. Since $\gamma \neq 0$,

$C \neq 0$. The similarity f restricted to A is a similarity of A onto an initial segment of β. Thus $\alpha < \beta$.

A 13.25 This is an immediate consequence of 13.24.

A 13.26 Let $(A, R), (B, S), (C, T)$ be disjoint well ordered sets similar respectively to α, β, and γ. There is a similarity f: $C \cup A$ $>\!\!\!\longrightarrow\!\!\!>$ $C \cup B$ of the ordinal sums. This similarity f must map C onto C, for otherwise $(f \mid C)$ or $(f^{-1} \mid C)$ is a similarity of a well ordered set onto an initial segment of itself. Thus $(f \mid A)$: $A >\!\!\!\longrightarrow\!\!\!> B$ shows A to be similar to B and therefore $\alpha = \beta$.

A 13.27 Suppose $\alpha + \gamma = \beta$ and $\alpha + \gamma' = \beta$. Then $\alpha + \gamma = \alpha + \gamma'$. By 13.26 $\gamma = \gamma'$.

A 13.28 $0 + \omega = 1 + \omega$ and $0 \neq 1$.

A 13.29 $\alpha + \delta = \beta$ for some $\delta \neq 0$. $(\gamma + \alpha) + \delta = \gamma + \beta$. $\gamma + \alpha < \gamma + \beta$.

A 13.30 An obvious consequence of 13.29.

A 13.31 The contrapositive of 13.30.

A 13.32 The contrapositive of 13.29.

A 13.33 Suppose $\beta + \gamma < \gamma$. Let B and C be disjoint sets similar respectively to β and γ. Then $B \cup C$ is similar by some bijection f to an initial segment of C, say $s(c)$. But $c \in C$ implies $c \in B \cup C$. $f(c) < c$. But any similarity of a well ordered set into itself must have $x \leq f(x)$ for all x. Contradiction.

A 13.34 Let δ be such that $\alpha + \delta = \beta$. $\gamma \leq \delta + \gamma$. $\alpha + \gamma \leq \alpha + \delta + \gamma$. $\alpha + \gamma \leq \beta + \gamma$.

A 13.35 $0 < 1$ and $0 + \omega = 1 + \omega$.

A 13.36 13.34 implies the contrapositive of the statement to be proven

A 13.37 $\alpha \cup \{\alpha\}$ is similar to $\beta \cup \{\beta\}$ by some similarity f. The last element α of α^+ must have image under f the last element β

of β^+. Therefore $f - \{(\alpha, \beta)\}$ is a similarity of α onto β. $\alpha = \beta$.

A 13.38 The proof is by induction on n. $\alpha + 0 < \beta + 0$. Assume $\alpha + n < \beta + n$. Then $(\alpha+n)^+ < (\beta+n)^+$. (Both $(\beta+n)^+ = (\alpha+n)^+$ and $(\beta+n)^+ > (\alpha+n)^+$ lead to contradictions.) $(\alpha+n) + 1 < (\beta+n) + 1$. $\alpha + (n+1) < \beta + (n+1)$. $\alpha + n^+ < \beta + n^+$.

A 13.39 $\alpha + \alpha = \alpha + 0$. By left cancellation $\alpha = 0$.

A 13.40 If $\alpha = \omega$ then $\alpha + \beta = \omega$ implies $\beta = 0$. But this is impossible if $\alpha\beta = \omega$. If α is finite, then β cannot be finite. If α is finite and $\beta = \omega$, then $\alpha + \beta = \omega$ and $\alpha\beta = \omega$.

A 13.41 $\alpha \times 0 = 0 \times \alpha = 0$.

A 13.42 Let $(x, 0), (y, 0) \in \alpha \times 1$. $(x, 0) < (y, 0)$ iff $x < y$ in the ordering of the ordinal product. $f\colon \alpha \times 1 >\!\!\longrightarrow\!\!>\!\!> \alpha$ such that $f(x, 0) = x$ is a similarity. In like manner, $1 \cdot \alpha = \alpha$.

A 13.43 $\alpha \times (\beta \times \gamma)$ and $(\alpha \times \beta) \times \gamma$ are clearly equivalent under the obvious bijection. That this bijection is a similarity is a consequence of the following: $(x_1, (y_1, z_1)) < (x_2, (y_2, z_2))$ iff
$(y_1, z_1) < (y_2, z_2)$ or $(x_1 < z_2$ and $(y_1, z_1) = (y_2, z_2))$ iff
$(z_1 < z_2$ or $(y_1 < y_2$ and $z_1 = z_2))$ or
$(x_1 < x_2$ and $(y_1 = y_2$ and $z_1 = z_2))$ iff
$((x_1 < x_2$ and $y_1 = y_2)$ or $y_1 < y_2)$ and $z_1 = z_2)$ or
$z_1 < z_2$ iff $((x_1, y_1) < (x_2, y_2)$ and $z_1 = z_2)$ or
$z_1 < z_2$ iff $((x_1, y_1), z_1) < ((x_2, y_2), z_2)$.

A 13.44 Let A, B, C be disjoint sets similar respectively to α, β, γ. $A \times (B \cup C) = (A \times B) \cup (A \times C)$. Let the order on set A be represented by $(<A)$. $(x_1, y_1)(<A \times (B \cup C))(x_2, y_2)$ iff
$[x_1(<A)x_2$ and $y_1 = y_2]$ or $y_1(<B \cup C)y_2$ iff
$[x_1(<A)x_2$ and $y_1 = y_2]$ or $y_1(<B)y_2$ or $y_1(<C)y_2$ or
$[y_1 \in B$ and $y_2 \in C]$ iff
$[(x_1(<A)x_2$ and $y_1 = y_2)$ or $y_1(<B)y_2]$ or
$[y_1 \in B$ and $y_2 \in C]$ or $[(x_1(<A)x_2$ and $y_1 = y_2)$ or $y_1(<C)y_2]$

iff $[(x_1, y_1)(<A\times B)(x_2, x_2)]$ or $[(x_1, y_1) \in A\times B$ and $(x_2, y_2) \in A\times C]$ or $[(x_1, y_1)(<A\times C)(x_2, y_2)]$ iff $(x_1, y_1)(<(A\times B)\cup(A\times C)(x_2, y_2)$.

A 13.45 $\gamma\alpha$ and $\gamma\beta$ are by definition similar to $\gamma\times\alpha$ and $\gamma\times\beta$ with the product orderings. $\alpha<\beta$ implies α is an initial segment of β, namely, $s(\text{minimum}(\beta-\alpha))$. $(x, y)\in\gamma\times\alpha$ iff $x\in\gamma$ and $y\in\alpha$ iff $x\in\gamma$ and $y\in\beta$ and $y<\min(\beta-\alpha)$ iff $(x, y)\in\gamma\times\beta$ and $y<\min(\beta-\alpha)$ iff $(x, y)\in\gamma\times\beta$ and $(x, y)<(0,\min(\beta-\alpha))$ iff $(x, y)\in s(0,\min(\beta-\alpha))$, an initial segment of $\gamma\times\beta$. Thus $\gamma\alpha$ is an initial segment of $\gamma\beta$.

A 13.46 For nonzero γ the contrapositive of 13.45 yields: if $\gamma\alpha\leq\gamma\beta$ then $\alpha\leq\beta$. Now suppose $\gamma\alpha<\gamma\beta$. Then $\alpha\leq\beta$. But if $\alpha=\beta$, we have $\gamma\alpha=\gamma\beta$. Therefore $\alpha<\beta$. The proposition is obviously true for $\gamma=0$.

A 13.47 Suppose $\alpha\neq\beta$. Then $\alpha<\beta$ and $\gamma>0$ imply $\gamma\alpha<\gamma\beta$. $\beta<\alpha$ and $\gamma>0$ imply $\gamma\beta<\gamma\alpha$. Therefore $\alpha=\beta$.

A 13.48 If f is a similarity of α onto an initial segment of β, then there exists a similarity F of $\alpha\times\gamma$ onto a subset of $\beta\times\gamma$ where $\alpha\times\gamma$ and $\beta\times\gamma$ have the product orderings and $F(x, y)=(f(x), y)$. If one assumes there is a similarity g of $\beta\times\gamma$ onto an initial segment of $\alpha\times\gamma$, then $g\circ F$ is a similarity of $\alpha\times\gamma$ onto a subset of an initial segment of $\alpha\times\gamma$. This is a contradiction, since no well ordered set can be similar to a subset of an initial segment of itself. Thus $\alpha\gamma\leq\beta\gamma$.

A 13.49 The contrapositive of the previous theorem is $\beta\gamma<\alpha\gamma$ implies $\beta\leq\alpha$. But if $\beta=\alpha$ then $\beta\gamma=\alpha\gamma$.

A 13.50 If $\beta\neq 0$ then $1\leq\beta$. Therefore $1\cdot\gamma\leq\beta\gamma$.

A 13.51 Let $\delta^+=\gamma$. $\alpha<\beta$ implies $\alpha\delta\leq\beta\delta$. Then $\alpha\delta+\alpha\leq\beta\delta+\alpha<\beta\delta+\beta$. $\alpha(\delta+1)<\beta(\delta+1)$. $\alpha\delta^+<\beta\delta^+$. $\alpha\gamma<\beta\gamma$.

A 13.52 If $\alpha<\beta$ then $\alpha\gamma<\beta\gamma$. If $\beta<\alpha$ then $\beta\gamma<\alpha\gamma$.

A 13.53 The contrapositive of the proposition is 13.52.

A 13.54 Since $\gamma < \alpha\beta$, ε is similar to an initial segment of $\alpha \times \beta$ (with the order of the ordinal product), say $s(a, b)$. $s(a, b) = \{(x, y) | y < b \text{ or } (x < a \text{ and } y = b)\} = \{(x, y) | y < b\} \cup \{(x, y) | x < a \text{ and } y = b\} = (\alpha \times \{y | y < b\}) \cup (\{x | x < a\} \times \{b\})$. The equalities can be replaced by similarities ($\simeq$) where the union is given the order of the ordinal sum; the product is given the order of the ordinal product. Thus $\varepsilon \simeq s(a, b) \simeq \alpha\beta_1 + \alpha_1 \cdot 1 = \alpha\beta_1 + \alpha_1$ with $\beta_1 < \beta$, $\alpha_1 < \alpha$. Now let $\varepsilon = \alpha\beta_2 + \alpha_2$ with $\beta_2 < \beta$, $\alpha_2 < \alpha$. Suppose $\beta_1 < \beta_2$. Then there exists a $\delta > 0$ so that $\beta_1 + \delta = \beta_2$. $\alpha\beta_2 + \alpha_2 = \alpha(\beta_1 + \delta) + \alpha_2 = \alpha\beta_1 + \alpha\delta + \alpha_2$. $\alpha\beta_1 + \alpha\delta + \alpha_2 = \alpha\beta_1 + \alpha_1$. By left cancellation $\alpha\delta + \alpha_2 = \alpha_1$. But $\delta > 0$ yields $\alpha \leq \alpha\delta \leq \alpha\delta + \alpha_2$ contradicting $\alpha_1 < \alpha$. Therefore, $\beta_1 < \beta_2$ is false. In like manner $\beta_2 < \beta_1$ cannot hold. Thus we have $\beta_1 = \beta_2$. $\alpha\beta_1 = \alpha\beta_2$ and from the equation $\alpha\beta_2 + \alpha_2 = \alpha\beta_1 + \alpha_1$ we left cancel and get $\alpha_2 = \alpha_1$ proving uniqueness.

A 13.55 $\beta \leq \alpha\beta$. If $\beta < \alpha\beta$ then $\beta = \varepsilon$ in the preceding theorem. Thus $\beta = \alpha\pi + \rho$ with $\pi < \beta$ and $\rho < \alpha$ and uniquely so. If $\beta = \alpha\beta$ then $\beta = \alpha\beta + 0$. If $\beta = \alpha\beta' + \alpha'$ with $\beta' < \beta$ and $\alpha' < \alpha$ as well as $\beta = \alpha\beta + 0$, then $\alpha\beta' + \alpha\delta = \alpha\beta' + \alpha'$, where $\beta = \beta' + \delta$. By left cancellation $\alpha\delta = \alpha'$. But $\delta \geq 1$ and $\alpha' < \alpha$ and $\alpha \leq \alpha\delta$ gives a contradiction.

A 13.56 First, let ω fail to be a left factor of β. $\beta = \omega\pi + \rho$ with $\pi \leq \beta$ and $0 < \rho < \omega$. $\rho \in \omega$; ρ is a nonzero natural number means there is a natural number σ so that $\sigma^+ = \rho$. Hence $(\omega\pi + \sigma)^+ = \omega\pi + \sigma^+ = \omega\pi + \rho = \beta$ by the associative law for ordinals. β is then not a limit ordinal.

Assume now that ω is a left factor of $\beta \neq 0$. $\beta = \omega\pi + 0$ with $\pi \leq \beta$. Suppose β is not a limit ordinal. Then $\beta = \gamma + 1$ for some ordinal γ. Upon left division by ω, $\gamma = \omega\sigma + \tau$ with $\sigma \leq \gamma$ and $\tau < \omega$. Thus $\omega\pi = \omega\sigma + \tau + 1$. If $\sigma = \pi$ then one left cancels $\omega\pi$ for a contradiction. If $\sigma < \pi$ then $\sigma + \varepsilon = \pi$ $(\varepsilon > 0)$ yielding

$\omega\sigma + \omega\varepsilon = \omega\sigma + \tau + 1$. $\omega\varepsilon = \tau + 1$. $\omega\varepsilon \geq \omega$ and $\tau + 1 < \omega$ since $\tau < \omega$ yielding a contradiction. If $\pi < \sigma$, then $\omega\pi < \omega\sigma$. $\omega\pi < \omega\sigma + \tau + 1$. Contradiction.

A 13.57 a) $\omega = 2\omega + 0$. b) $\omega + 1 = 2\omega + 1$.
c) $1 + \omega = \omega = 2\omega + 0$. d) $(\omega+1)^2 = (\omega+1)\omega + \omega + 1 = \omega\omega + 1 + \omega + 1 = \omega^2 + \omega + 1 = \omega(\omega+1) + 1 = 2[\omega(\omega+1)] + 1$.
e) $(\omega+1)2 = \omega 2 + 1 = (2\omega)2 + 1 + 2(\omega 2) + 1$.

A 13.58 As the ordinal sequence assigns to each element i of a set of ordinals μ a unique ordinal a_i, there is, by the axiom of substitution, a function a with domain μ such that image $a = \{a_i | i \in \mu\}$ is a set. Since image a is a set of ordinals, it has a supremum which is an ordinal.

A 13.59 Suppose $(a_i)_{i \in \mu}$ is an increasing ordinal sequence and let $\sup\{a_i | i \in \mu\} = \lambda$. Let (γ, δ) be a neighborhood of λ. $\gamma < \lambda < \delta$. Suppose $a_i \leq \gamma$ for all $i \in \mu$. Then γ is the $\sup\{a_i | i \in \mu\}$, which cannot be. Therefore $\gamma < a_\nu$ for some $\nu \in \mu$. But $(a_i)_{i \in \mu}$ is increasing. $\gamma < a_\nu \leq a_i \leq \lambda < \delta$ for all $i \in \mu$, $i > \nu$. $(a_i)_{i \in \mu}$ is eventually in (γ, δ).

Conversely, suppose $(a_i)_{i \in \mu}$ is eventually in every neighborhood of λ. Since $(0, \lambda + 1)$ is a neighborhoodof λ (unless $\lambda = 0$ a trivial case) and $(a_i)_{i \in \mu}$ is eventually in $(0, \lambda + 1)$, λ is an upper bound fro $(a_i)_{i \in \mu}$. If λ' were a smaller upper bound, then the neighborhood $(\lambda', \lambda + 1)$ would be empty, contradicting the hypothesis. $\lambda = \sup\{a_i | i \in \mu\}$.

A 13.60 If $a = (a_i)_{i \in \mu}$ is a strictly increasing ordinal sequence, then $a\colon \mu \to \{a_i | i \in \mu\}$. If $i, j \in \mu$ and $i < j$, then $a_i < a_j$. Suppose on the other hand that $a_i < a_j$. $i < j$ or $i = j$ or $j < i$. If $i = j$ then $a_i = a_j$. If $j < i$ then $a_j < a_i$. Thus $i < j$.

A 13.61 Similarities on well ordered sets are unique.

A 13.62 $a_i = i$, $\beta_i = i$, $\mu = \omega$.

A 13.63 2^ω is an uncountable set by Cantor's theorem. 2^ω can be well ordered by the well-ordering theorem. Let γ be the ordinal similar to the well ordered set 2^ω. Let $\Gamma = \{x \mid x \in \gamma$ and x is uncountable$\}$. Let $\Omega = \bigcap\Gamma$. Since Ω is the minimum of the set Γ if $\alpha < \Omega$, then α is not uncountable.

A 13.64 If A is a countable set, then $\sup A = \bigcup A$ is the countable union of countable sets and thus countable. Therefore $\sup A < \Omega$.

A 13.65 In every neighborhood of Ω there are members of Ω^+ in addition to Ω itself; yet if $(a_i)_{i \in \omega}$ is an increasing sequence with values in Ω the sequence cannot have Ω as a limit $(\sup\{a_i \mid i \in \omega\} < \Omega)$.

A 13.66 Let $a_j = \lim_{i \in \mu} a_i$ for some $j \in \mu$. Then $j + 1 \in \mu$ because if $j + 1 = \mu$, then μ would not be a limit ordinal. But $a_{j+1} > a_j = \lim_{i \in \mu} a_i$, a contradiction.

Suppose $\lambda = \lim_{i \in \mu} a_i$ is not a limit ordinal. Since $\lambda \neq 0$, there exists an ordinal ν so that $\nu + 1 = \lambda$. But $\nu < \lambda$ and therefore $a_i > \nu$ for some $i \in \mu$ since λ is the supremum. $a_i = \lambda$. Contradiction.

A 13.67 $\mu = \nu + 1$ for some ordinal ν. ν is the last or maximum element of μ. Thus a_ν is the last term of the ordinal sequence. If $i < \nu$ then $a_i < a_\nu$. $\sup\{a_i \mid i \in \mu\} = a_\nu$.

The ordinal sequence $(0, 1, 2, \ldots, \omega)$ has as its limit ω, which is a limit ordinal and is indexed by $\omega + 1$, which is not a limit ordinal.

A 13.68 $(a_i)_{i \in \mu}$ has a last term a_ν where $\nu + 1 = \mu$. Provided $i \geq \nu$, a_i belongs to every neighborhood of a_ν. a_ν is the limit. On the other hand, the sequence $(a_i)_{i \in \omega}$, $a_i = 1$ for i even, $= 0$ for i odd, has no limit.

A 13.69 The ordinal $\sup\{a_j \mid j \in \mu\}$ exists, since every set of ordinals has an ordinal supremum. $a_i \leq \sup\{a_j \mid j \in \mu\}$ for all $i \in \mu$.

Therefore $\gamma + a_i \leq \gamma + \sup\{a_j | j \in \mu\}$ for all $i \in \mu$. Therefore $\gamma + \sup\{a_j | j \in \mu\}$ is an upper bound for $(\gamma + a_i)_{i \in \mu}$.

On the other hand, suppose that β is an ordinal so that $\gamma + a_i \leq \beta$ for all $i \in \mu$. Then $\gamma \leq \beta$ and there exists a δ such that $\gamma + \delta = \beta$. $\gamma + a_i \leq \gamma + \delta$ for all $i \in \mu$. $a_i \leq \delta$ for all $i \in \mu$. $\sup\{a_i | i \in \mu\} \leq \delta$. $\gamma + \sup\{a_i | i \in \mu\} \leq \gamma + \delta = \beta$. Therefore $\gamma + \sup\{a_i | i \in \mu\} = \sup\{\gamma + a_i | i \in \mu\}$.

A 13.70 If $\mu = 0$ the proposition is true. If μ is not zero and is not a limit ordinal, the proof is trivial. If $\gamma = 0$ the conclusion is true. Now suppose μ is a limit ordinal and $\gamma \neq 0$.

$\sup\{a_j | j \in \mu\}$ is an ordinal and $a_i \leq \sup\{a_j | j \in \mu\}$ for all $i \in \mu$. $\gamma a_i \leq \gamma \sup\{a_j | j \in \mu\}$ for all $i \in \mu$, proving $\gamma \sup\{a_j | j \in \mu\}$ is an upper bound for $(\gamma a_i)_{i \in \mu}$.

On the other hand, suppose β is any other upper bound for $(\gamma a_i)_{i \in \mu}$. $\gamma a_i \leq \beta$ for all $i \in \mu$. Then $\gamma < \beta$. Therefore $\beta = \gamma\pi + \rho$ with $\rho < \gamma$. $\gamma(\pi + 1) = \gamma\pi + \gamma > \gamma\pi + \rho = \beta \geq \gamma a_i$ for all $i \in \mu$. $\gamma(\pi + 1) > \gamma a_i$ for all $i \in \mu$. $\pi + 1 > a_i$ for all $i \in \mu$. $\pi + 1 \geq \sup\{a_i | i \in \mu\}$, since the supremum is the minimum of the set of all upper bounds. Since $\sup\{a_i | i \in \mu\}$ is a limit ordinal (13.66) it cannot equal $\pi + 1$. $\pi + 1 > \sup\{a_i | i \in \mu\}$. $\pi \geq \sup\{a_i | i \in \mu\}$. $\gamma\pi \geq \gamma \sup\{a_i | i \in \mu\}$. $\beta = \gamma\pi + \rho \geq \gamma\pi \geq \gamma \sup\{a_i | i \in \mu\}$.

A 13.71 Let $(a_i)_{i \in \omega} = (i)_{i \in \omega}$, $\gamma = \omega$. $\gamma + \sup\{i | i \in \omega\} = \omega + \omega$
$\sup\{i + \omega | i \in \omega\} = \sup\{\omega\} = \omega$.

A 13.72 Same values as in 13.71.

$$\sup\{i | i \in \omega\} \cdot \omega = \omega \cdot \omega = \omega^2.$$
$$\sup\{i\omega | i \in \omega\} = \sup\{\omega\} = \omega.$$

A 13.73 Suppose that $S(a)$ is false for some ordinal a. Let $B = \{x | x \leq a \text{ and } S(x) \text{ is false}\}$ which exists by the axiom of specification. Every set of ordinals is well ordered and therefore B has a minimum γ. For every $x < \gamma$, $S(x)$. Thus by hypothesis it follows that $S(\gamma)$. This contradiction establishes the conclusion.

A 13.74 Suppose that for some ordinal γ the conclusion is false.

Let $C = \{x \mid x \leq \gamma$ and the conclusion is false for the ordinal $x\}$. Let δ = minimum C. For each $x \epsilon \delta$ there exists a unique ordinal $u(x)$ such that $u(x) = f(u \mid x)$ where $u \mid x = \{(\beta, u(\beta)) \mid \beta \epsilon x\}$. $\{(\beta, u(\beta)) \mid \beta \epsilon \delta\}$ is a function by the axiom of substitution and is the set $u \mid \delta$. Thus there exists a unique ordinal $f(u \mid \delta) = u(\delta)$, and the conclusion is true for δ. This contradiction establishes the theorem.

A 13.75 If the conclusion of the proposition is false for some ordinal, let δ be the minimum ordinal for which the conclusion is false. $\delta \neq 0$ since $a = u(0)$ is a unique ordinal and $u \mid 0 = 0$ is a function satisfying the conclusion of the proposition. If $\delta = \varepsilon^+$ for some ordinal ε, then $u(x)$ is a unique ordinal for each $x \leq \varepsilon$. $u(\varepsilon)$ is a unique ordinal and thus $g(u(\varepsilon)) = u(\delta)$ is a unique ordinal. $\{(\beta, u(\beta)) \mid \beta \epsilon \delta\} = u \mid \delta$ is a function by the axiom of substitution. Thus δ satisfies the conclusion of the proposition, and therefore $\delta \neq \varepsilon^+$ for any ordinal ε. Now finally let δ be a limit ordinal. $u(x)$ is a unique ordinal for each $x < \delta$. $(u(x))_{x \epsilon \delta} = u \mid \delta$ is a function and image $(u(x))_{x \epsilon \delta} = \{u(x) \mid x \epsilon \delta\}$ is a set by the axiom of substitution. $\sup\{u(x) \mid x \epsilon \delta\} = u(\delta)$ is a unique ordinal. Therefore δ cannot be a limit ordinal. There can be no ordinal for which the conclusion of the proposition is false.

A 13.76 In 13.75 let $u = s_\alpha$, $a = \alpha$, $g(\xi) = \xi^+$.

A 13.77 $s_\alpha(0) = \alpha$ and $\alpha + 0 = \alpha$. $s_\alpha(\beta) = s_\alpha(\delta^+) = [s_\alpha(\delta)]^+ = (\alpha+\delta) + 1 = \alpha + (\delta+1) = \alpha + \delta^+ = \alpha + \beta$ if $\beta = \delta^+$. $s_\alpha(\beta) = \sup\{s_\alpha(\zeta) \mid \zeta \epsilon \beta\} = \sup\{\alpha + \zeta \mid \zeta \epsilon \beta\} = \alpha + \sup\{\zeta \mid \zeta \epsilon \beta\} = \alpha + \beta$ if β is a limit ordinal using 13.69. By the uniqueness of the assignment defined in 13.75, $s_\alpha(\beta) = \alpha + \beta$ for all β.

A 13.78 In 13.75 let $u = p_\alpha$, $a = 0$, $g(\xi) = \xi + \alpha$.

A 13.79 $p_\alpha(0) = 0$ and $\alpha \cdot 0 = 0$. If $\beta = \delta^+$ then $p_\alpha(\beta) = p_\alpha(\delta^+) = p_\alpha(\delta) + \alpha = \alpha\delta + \alpha = \alpha\delta + \alpha \cdot 1 = \alpha(\delta+1) = \alpha\delta^+ = \alpha\beta$. If β is a limit ordinal, $p_\alpha(\beta) = \sup\{p_\alpha(\zeta) \mid \zeta < \beta\} = \sup\{\alpha\zeta \mid \zeta < \beta\} =$

$= \alpha \sup\{\zeta \mid \zeta < \beta\} = \alpha\beta$. By the uniqueness of the ordinals defined, $p_\alpha(\beta) = \alpha\beta$, for all β.

A 13.80 Again 13.75 with $u(\beta) = \alpha^\beta$, $a = 1$, $g(\xi) = \xi\alpha$.

A 13.81 This is a definition by transfinite recursion on the well ordered set μ^+. Cf. p. 70 of NST. $W = \mu^+$. Let $\nu \in \mu^+$. Then $f((\beta_j)_{j\in\nu}) = 0$ if $\nu = 0$, $f((\beta_j)_{j\in\nu}) = \beta_\pi + \alpha_\nu$ if $\nu = \pi^+$ and $f((\beta_j)_{j\in\nu}) = \sup\{\beta_j \mid j \in \nu\}$ if ν is a limit ordinal. $U(\nu) = \Sigma_{i\in\nu}\, \alpha_i$, the ν-th partial sum.

A 13.82 Let δ be the smallest ordinal for which $\Sigma_{i\in\delta}\, \alpha$ and $\alpha \cdot \delta$ do not agree. $\delta \neq 0$ since $\Sigma_{i\in 0}\, \alpha = 0$ and $\alpha \cdot 0 = 0$. If $\delta = \epsilon^+$ then $\Sigma_{i\in\delta}\, \alpha = \Sigma_{i\in\varepsilon^+}\, \alpha = \Sigma_{i\in\varepsilon}\, \alpha + \alpha = \alpha\varepsilon + \alpha = \alpha(\varepsilon + 1) = \alpha \cdot \varepsilon^+ = \alpha\delta$. Therefore $\delta \neq \varepsilon^+$. If δ is a limit ordinal, then $\Sigma_{i\in\delta}\, \alpha = \sup\{\Sigma_{i\in\zeta}\, \alpha \mid \zeta < \delta\} = \sup\{\alpha\zeta \mid \zeta \in \delta\} = \alpha \sup\{\zeta \mid \zeta \in \delta\} = \alpha\delta$, which is impossible. Hence $\Sigma_{i\in\mu}\alpha = \alpha\mu$ for all ordinal μ.

A 13.83 $\Sigma_{i\in k}\, \omega = \omega k$ for $k \in \omega$. $\sup\{\omega k \mid k \in \omega\} = \omega^2$.

A 13.84 $\omega^2 + \omega$.

A 13.85 Compare with 13.81.

A 13.86 Compare with 13.82. Some details are $\Pi_{i\in 0}\, \alpha = 1$, $\alpha^0 = 1$
$\Pi_{i\in\beta}\, \alpha = \Pi_{i\in\delta^+}\, \alpha = (\Pi_{i\in\delta}\, \alpha)\alpha = \alpha^\delta \cdot \alpha = \alpha^{\delta^+} = \alpha^\beta$.
$\Pi_{i\in\beta}\, \alpha = \sup\{\Pi_{i\in\zeta}\, \alpha \mid \zeta \in \beta\} = \sup\{\alpha^\zeta \mid \zeta \in \beta\} = \alpha^\beta$.

A 13.87 $\Sigma_{i\in k^+}\, \omega^i = \omega^k$, $\sup\{\omega^k \mid k \in \omega\} = \omega^\omega$.

A 13.88 The ordering by last differences does not, in general, totally order $\mathsf{X}_{i\in\mu}\, \alpha_i$.

A 13.89 $\omega^{\varepsilon_0} = \sup\{\omega^{\alpha_i} \mid i \in \omega\} = \sup\{\alpha_{i^+} \mid i \in \omega\} = \varepsilon_0$.

A 14.1 a) The identity function I_X: $X >\!\!\longrightarrow\!\!> X$ proves that X dominates X. b) Let $f: X >\!\!\longrightarrow Y$ and $g: Y >\!\!\longrightarrow Z$. Then $g \circ f: X >\!\!\longrightarrow Z$. Cf. 4.29. c) The Schröder-Bernstein theorem. d) $Y = \mathcal{P}X$. e) Page 89 of NST or Exercise 14.4.

A 14.2 n is a subset of ω and therefore ω dominates n. Suppose ω were equivalent to n. But the n^+ strictly dominates n and by transitivity would also strictly dominate ω. This is impossible since ω dominates n^+.

A 14.3 Let X, Y be two sets. Let $\mathcal{S} = \{S \mid S$ is a bijection from a subset of X to a subset of $Y\}$. $\mathcal{S} \neq \emptyset$ since $\emptyset \in \mathcal{S}$. $\mathcal{S}$ is ordered by inclusion. Let $\mathcal{C}$ be a chain in $\mathcal{S}$. $\bigcup \mathcal{C}$ is a bijection. $\mathcal{S}$ has a maximal element M. Either domain $M = X$ or image $M = Y$. Suppose not. $a \in X$, $b \in Y$; $a \notin$ domain M, $b \notin$ image M. Then $M \cup \{(a, b)\}$ is greater than M. Contradiction.

A 14.4 Define $f: \mathrm{R} >\!\!\longrightarrow\!\!> (0, 1)$ such that $f(x) = (\tfrac{1}{2})(1 + x/(1 + |x|))$ and verify that f is a bijection. Define g: $[0, 1) >\!\!\longrightarrow\!\!> (0, 1)$ such that $g(0) = 1/2$, $g(1/n) = 1/(n+1)$ for $n = 2, 3, \ldots$, $g(x) = x$ otherwise and verify that g is a bijection.

A 14.5 If $f: X_1 >\!\!\longrightarrow\!\!> X_2$ and $g: Y_1 >\!\!\longrightarrow\!\!> Y_2$, then $f \cup g$: $X_1 \cup Y_1 >\!\!\longrightarrow\!\!> X_2 \cup Y_2$. (Proof ?)

A 14.6 If $f: A >\!\!\longrightarrow\!\!> C$ and $g: B >\!\!\longrightarrow\!\!> D$, then $h: A \times B >\!\!\longrightarrow\!\!> C \times D$ such that $h(a, b) = (f(a), g(b))$. (Proof?)

A 14.7 The following identities for sets are crucial for proving the required statements: $A \cup B = B \cup A$, $A \cup (B \cup C) = (A \cup B) \cup C$, $A \times B \sim B \times A$, $A \times (B \times C) \sim (A \times B) \times C$, $A \times (B \cup C) = (A \times B) \cup (A \times C)$.

A 14.8 Let card $A = a$, card $B = b$, card $C = c$ such that $A \cap C = B \cap C = \emptyset$. Let $f: A >\!\!\longrightarrow B$. Then $f \cup I_C$: $A \cup C >\!\!\longrightarrow B \cup C$. (Proof?)

A 14.9 Let $f: A >\!\!\longrightarrow B$ where $\operatorname{card} A = a$ and $\operatorname{card} B = b$. Then $h: A \times C >\!\!\longrightarrow B \times C$ such that $h(a, c) = (h(a), c)$. (Proof?)

A 14.10 $ab \sim a \times b = \bigcup_{i \in b} a \times \{i\} \sim \Sigma_{i \in b}\, a$.

A 14.11 $\Pi_{i \in b}\, a \sim \mathsf{X}_{i \in b}\, a = \{f \mid f \in a^b \text{ and } f(i) \in a\} = \{f \mid f \in a^b\} a^b$.

A 14.12 In Section 4 are exercises in which are proven $A^{B \cup C} \sim A^B \times A^C$, $(A \times B)^C \sim A^C \times B^C$, $(A^B)^C \sim A^{B \times C}$.

A 14.13 The existence of an injection $g: A >\!\!\longrightarrow B$ allows one to define in a natural way an injection $h: A^D >\!\!\longrightarrow B^D$ such that $h(f) = g \circ f$. Compare with 4.10 and furnish the details.

A 14.14 If $a < b$ then $b = a \cup (b - a)$ with $b - a \neq 0$. $d \neq 0$ means $0 \in d$. Define $h: d^a >\!\!\longrightarrow d^b$ such that $h(f) = f \cup \{(x, 0) \mid x \in b - a\}$. Verify that h is an injection. Use the contrapositive to prove the second proposition.

A 14.15 Suppose that a, an infinite cardinal, is not a limit ordinal. Let $a = \beta^+$. β is infinite because the successor of a finite ordinal is finite. $\omega \subset \beta$. Define $f: \beta >\!\!\longrightarrow\!\!> \beta - \{0\}$ as follows: $f(x) = x^+$ if $x \in \omega$ and $f(x) = x$ if $x \in \beta - \omega$. $f \cup \{(\beta, 0)\}: \beta^+ >\!\!\longrightarrow\!\!> \beta$. Thus we have proven that $a = \beta^+$ is equivalent to β. a is then not a cardinal number.

A 14.16 There is but one function from ω to 1 or from c to 1 and therefore $1^\omega = 1^\mathrm{c} = 1$. That $\omega + \omega$ and $\omega\omega$ are both equal to ω follows from theorems on pp. 96, 97 of NST. The inequality $0 + \omega \leq n + \omega \leq \omega + \omega = \omega$ establishes $n + \omega = \omega$. $1\omega \leq n\omega \leq \omega\omega$ proves $n\omega = \omega$. Prove $\omega^n = \omega$ by induction on n. $\mathrm{c} + \mathrm{c} = \mathrm{c}$, $\mathrm{cc} = \mathrm{c}$, pp. 96, 97 of NST again. $0 + \mathrm{c} \leq n + \mathrm{c} \leq \omega + \mathrm{c} \leq \mathrm{c} + \mathrm{c} = \mathrm{c}$. $1\mathrm{c} \leq n\mathrm{c} \leq \omega\mathrm{c} \leq \mathrm{cc} = \mathrm{c}$. $\mathrm{c} \leq \mathrm{c}^n \leq \mathrm{c}^\omega = (2^\omega)^\omega = 2^{\omega\omega} = 2^\omega = \mathrm{c}$.
$\mathrm{c} = 2^\omega \leq (n+1)^\omega \leq \omega^\omega \leq \mathrm{c}^\omega = \mathrm{c}$.
$2^\mathrm{c} \leq (n+1)^\mathrm{c} \leq \omega^\mathrm{c} \leq \mathrm{c}^\mathrm{c} \leq (2^\mathrm{c})^\mathrm{c} = 2^\mathrm{c}$.

A 14.17 $a_j \leq \Sigma_{i \in I}\, a_i$ for all $j \in I$. If $a_j = \Sigma_{i \in I}\, a_i$ for some $j \in I$, then a_j would be a maximum contradicting the assumption.

A14.18 Define $g(0)$ to be ω. If $g(n)$ is a set, define $g(n^+)$ to be the set $2^{g(n)}$. Then for all $n \in \omega$ there is defined a cardinal number $g(n)$, According to the axiom of substitution, if $A = \omega$ is a set and $S(a, b) = (b \in g(a))$ is a condition, then there exists a function $(g(a))_{a \in \omega}$ such that $g(a) = \{b \mid S(a, b)\} = \{b \mid b \in g(a)\} = g(a)$. This family is a nonfinite, countable family of distinct cardinal numbers.

A14.19 The family defined in 14.18 has no largest member. Thus $\Sigma_{n \in \omega}\, g(n)$ is larger than every value in g and distinct from each one. The set of all cardinals strictly greater than every cardinal in the sequence and less than or equal to $\Sigma_{n \in \omega}\, g(n)$ is nonempty. Any set of cardinals is well ordered. There is a least cardinal strictly greater than any cardinal in the sequence.

A14.20 $2^d \leq a^d \leq d^d \leq (2^d)^d \leq 2^{dd} \leq 2^d$. $a^d = 2^d$. Likewise $b^d = 2^d$.

A14.21 $c = 1 \cdot 2^{\omega} \leq \Pi_{i \in \omega^+ - \{0\}}\, i \leq \omega^{\omega} = c$.

A14.22 $1 \cdot 2^c \leq \Pi_{i \in c^+ - \{0\}}\, i \leq c^c = 2^c$.

A14.23 If $a < d$ and $b < d$, then $ab = \max\{a, b\} < d$. Why does $ab = \max\{a, b\}$?

A14.24 $\mathbf{Z} = \{0, 1, 2, \ldots\} \cup \{-1, -2, -3, \ldots\}$. Obviously card$\{-1, -2, \ldots\} = \omega$. card $\mathbf{Z} = \omega + \omega = \omega$.

A14.25 $f\colon \mathbf{Q} \rightarrowtail \mathbf{Z} \times \mathbf{Z}$ such that $f(a/b) = (a, b)$, where a/b is a member of $\mathbf{Q}$ expressed in lowest terms. $\mathbf{Q}$ is dominated by $\mathbf{Z} \times \mathbf{Z}$. card $\mathbf{Q} \leq$ card $\mathbf{Z} \times \mathbf{Z} = \omega \cdot \omega = \omega$. On the other hand, $\mathbf{Q}$ dominates ω. card $\mathbf{Q} \geq \omega$.

A14.26 There are ω constant polynomials with coefficients in $\mathbf{Q}$, and there are ω^2 1st degree polynomials. There are ω^{n+1} nth-degree polynomials. In all there are $\omega + \omega^2 + \cdots + \omega^{n+1} + \cdots$ polynomials. $\omega + \omega^2 + \cdots + \omega^{n+1} + \cdots = \omega + \omega + \cdots + \omega + \cdots = \omega \cdot \omega = \omega$.

A 14.27 Let A be the set of algebraic numbers. There are to each of the ω polynomials of degree n with rational coefficients (cf. 14.26) at most n roots. Thus all the polynomials of degree n can contribute at most $\omega \cdot n = \omega$ different algebraic numbers. In all, counting all degrees, there can be at most $\omega \cdot \omega = \omega$ different algebraic numbers. card $A \leq \omega$. But each member q of $\mathbf{Q}$ being a root of $X - q$ is an algebraic number. card $A \geq \omega$.

A 14.28 From 7.19 card $\mathbf{R} \leq$ card $\mathbf{Q}^{\mathbf{N}} \leq \omega^{\omega} = 2^{\omega}$. A subset P of consisting of all the real numbers expressible in the *decimal* (base 10) form $0.r_1 r_2 r_3 \ldots$ in which $r_i = 0$ or 1 for all $i \in \omega$ has card $P = 2^{\omega}$. Hence card $\mathbf{R} \geq$ card $P = 2^{\omega}$.

A 14.29 The number of continuous functions from $\mathbf{R}$ to $\mathbf{R}$ is the same as the number of continuous functions from $\mathbf{Q}$ to $\mathbf{R}$ because the values for irrational arguments are uniquely determined by the values for the rational arguments. Cf. Kelley's *General Topology* or some advanced calculus text. Thus the cardinality of the continuous function from $\mathbf{R}$ to $\mathbf{R}$ is less than or equal to card $\mathbf{R}^{\mathbf{Q}} = c^{\omega} = c$. Since there are c constant functions from $\mathbf{R}$ to $\mathbf{R}$, the cardinality of the set of continuous functions from $\mathbf{R}$ to $\mathbf{R}$ is exactly c.

A 14.30 Suppose card$(A-B) <$ card A. $(A-B) \cap B = \emptyset$, yielding card A = card$(A-B) \cup B$ = card$(A-B)$ + card B = max{card$(A-B)$, card B} $<$ card A, since both card $A-B$ and card B were assumed $<$ card A. It is therefore established that card$(A-B) \geq$ card A. But A dominates $A-B$ with the identity injection. card $A \geq$ card$(A-B)$.

A 14.31 If both card X and card Y are finite, then the theorem is given as proven. If card $X = n$, finite, and card $Y \geq \omega$, then choose $n+1$ vectors from the basis Y. Since card $X = n$, these $n+1$ vectors, all independent, would have to be dependent. This is impossible. Now assume both card X and card Y are infinite. We count the possible number of linear independent combinations we can form using the basis X. Of length 1 we have a choice of any multiple of any one of the n members of X, but of course for a given member of X only one nonzero multiple can be counted, yielding n possible linear combinations. Of length 2 we have $\leq n \cdot n$ possible choices for the two vectors and at most 2 different combinations which are linearly independent for each pair of vectors chosen. The number of combinations of length 2 is $\leq n^2 \cdot 2$. Thus of all lengths $(< \omega)$ one has $\leq n + 2n^2 + 2n^3 + \cdots$ different linear independent combinations. Any member of Y is expressible as one of these combinations since X is a basis. Thus we have card $Y \leq n + 2n^2 + 3n^3 + \cdots = n + n + n + \cdots = \omega n = n$. card $Y \leq$ card X. In like manner, card $X \leq$ card Y.

A 14.32 Let $(a_i)_{i \epsilon \omega}$ be a strictly increasing sequence of infinite cardinal numbers (one was constructed in 14.18). Then $a_0 + a_1 + a_2 + \cdots < a_0 a_1 a_2 \cdots$ by König's theorem (Exercise p. 95 of NST). Let $a = a_0 + a_1 + a_2 + \cdots$. $a > a_i$ for all $i \epsilon \omega$. Then $a < a_0 a_1 a_2 \cdots < a a a \cdots = a^{\omega}$.

Given any infinite cardinal γ, $\gamma + 2^{\gamma} + 2^{2^{\gamma}} + \cdots$ will be a strictly larger cardinal and have the property desired. An application of the axiom of substitution will produce an infinite set of these cardinals.

A 14.33 Let a be any cardinal number and let $a^{\omega} = \beta$. Then $\beta^{\omega} = (a^{\omega})^{\omega} = a^{\omega\omega} = a^{\omega} = \beta$. Then 2^{β} is a larger cardinal, a new a, and the process can be continued.

A 14.34 Let card $S = \omega$. Any operation is a function from $S \times S$ to S. There are $\omega^{\omega \cdot \omega}$ or c such operations. Therefore there are at most c groups (not every operation leads to a group but every group has an operation). Since **Z** is countable (**Z** is a group), each member of S may be identified with a member of **Z** (by some equivalence) yielding a group for S; moreover, this assignment composed with any permutation of S (of which there are $\omega! =$ c) yields another group for S. Hence there are at least c groups for S.

A 14.35 There are $\omega^n = \omega$ subsets of cardinality n $(n \in \omega)$. If for each $n \in \omega$ there are ω subsets, then there are $\omega \cdot \omega = \omega$ subsets in all which are finite.

A 14.36 There are $\mathfrak{c}^n = \mathfrak{c}$ subsets of cardinality n $(n \in \omega)$. In all there are $\omega \mathfrak{c} = \mathfrak{c}$ subsets which are finite. There are $\mathfrak{c}^\omega = \mathfrak{c}$ subsets which are of cardinality ω. There are then $\mathfrak{c}$ subsets $(= \mathfrak{c} + \mathfrak{c})$ which are countable.

A 14.37 There are a^b subsets of cardinality b. $a \leq a^b = (2^{\mathfrak{e}})^b = 2^{\mathfrak{e}} = a$. Thus there are a subsets of cardinality b. For each subset of cardinality b there are at most 2^b subsets of cardinality $\leq b$. Hence of cardinality $\leq b$ there are $a \cdot 2^b = a$ subsets.

A 14.38 The cardinal a in 14.32.

A 14.39 There are ω finite subsets of ω. For each member of a given finite subset there are ω possible nonzero values for a function. There are then $\omega^n = \omega$ possible functions nonzero on a given finite subset and zero elsewhere. There are therefore $\omega \cdot \omega = \omega$ members of $\mathcal{F}$.

REFERENCES

1 P. Halmos, *Naive Set Theory*. Van Nostrand: Princeton, 1960.

Other General Texts in Set Theory

2 P. Bernays and A. Fraenkel, *Axiomatic Set Theory*. North Holland Publishing Company: Amsterdam, 1958.

3 N. Bourbaki, *Théorie des Ensembles*. Herman: Paris, 1939.

4 A. Fraenkel, *Abstract Set Theory*. North Holland: Amsterdam, 1961.

5 J. Kelley, *General Topology*, Chapter 0 and Appendix. Van Nostrand: Princeton, 1955.

6 W. Sierpinski, *Algèbre des Ensembles*. Warszawa-Wroclaw, 1951.

7 R. Stoll, *Introduction to Logic and Set Theory*. Freeman: San Francisco, 1961.

8 P. Suppes, *Axiomatic Set Theory*. Van Nostrand: Princeton, 1960.

Older Classics in Set Theory

9 F. Hausdorff, *Set Theory*. Chelsea: New York City, 1937.

10 E. Kamke, *Theory of Sets*. Dover: New York City.

A Study of the Foundations of Set Theory

11 A. Fraenkel and Y. Bar-Hillel, *Foundations of Set Theory*. North Holland: Amsterdam, 1958.

Works Especially Devoted to Ordinals and Cardinals

12 H. Bachmann, *Transfinite Zahlen*. Springer: Berlin, 1955.

13 W. Sierpinski, *Cardinal and Ordinal Numbers*. Hafner: New York City, 1958.

Texts in Logic

14 E. Mendelson, *Introduction to Mathematical Logic*. Van Nostrand: Princeton, 1963.

15 P. Suppes, *Introduction to Logic*. Van Nostrand: Princeton, 1957.

Texts in Linear Algebra, Vector Spaces and Matrices

16 P. Halmos, *Finite Dimensional Vector Spaces*. Van Nostrand: Princeton, 1958.

17 F. Stewart, *Introduction to Linear Algebra*. Van Nostrand: Princeton, 1963.

Texts in Modern Algebra

18 W. Barnes, *Introduction to Abstract Algebra*. Heath: Boston, 1963.

19 G. Birkhoff and S. MacLane, *A Survey of Modern Algebra*. Macmillan: New York City, 1941.

A More Advanced Algebra Text

20 C. Chevalley, *Fundamental Concepts of Algebra*. Academic: New York City, 1957.